OTTO HAHN: , 1879-

A Scientific Autobiography

Translated and edited by *WILLY LEY*

Introduction by GLENN T. SEABORG, Chairman
of the United States Atomic Energy Commission

CHARLES SCRIBNER'S SONS
New York

CONTENTS

ILLUSTRATIONS

ILLUSTRATIONS

Max Planck and Otto Hahn, 1946
Glenn T. Seaborg
Otto Hahn, 1955

TABLES

Introduction

BY GLENN T. SEABORG

It has been given to very few men to make contributions to science and to humanity of the magnitude of those made by Otto Hahn. He has made those contributions over a span of nearly two generations, beginning with a key role in the earliest days of radiochemistry in investigating and unraveling the complexities of the natural radioactivities and culminating with his tremendous discovery of the nuclear fission of uranium.

I believe that it is fair to refer to Otto Hahn as the father of radiochemistry and of its more recent offspring, nuclear chemistry. As a young graduate student at the University of California at Berkeley in the mid-1930s and in connection with our work with plutonium a few years later, I used his book, *Applied Radiochemistry*, as my bible. This book was based on a series of lectures which Professor Hahn had given at Cornell University in 1933; it set forth the "laws" for the co-precipitation of minute quantities of radioactive materials when insoluble substances were precipitated from aqueous solutions. I recall reading and rereading every word in these "laws" of co-precipitation many times, attempting to derive every possible bit of guidance for our work, and perhaps in my zealousness reading into them more than the master himself had intended. I doubt that I have read sections in any other book more carefully or more frequently than those in Hahn's *Applied Radiochemistry*. In fact, I read the entire volume repeatedly and I recall that my chief disappointment with it was its length. It was too short.

Soon after the completion of my graduate work in nuclear chemistry at Berkeley, while I was serving as personal research assistant to another great chemist, Gilbert Newton Lewis, I learned of the word that had just come out of Germany concerning the exciting discovery of the fission of the uranium nucleus.

My graduate work, although carried on in the College of Chemistry, had been in the field of nuclear physics, and despite the fact that I was working with Lewis in the field of generalized acids and bases, rather far removed from radiochemistry or nuclear physics, I was also carrying on research with artificial radioactive isotopes, using the cyclotron of Ernest O. Lawrence. From the beginning I had a special interest in the work that was being carried on in Europe, first by Enrico Fermi and his coworkers in Rome, and then by Otto Hahn, Lise Meitner, and Fritz Strassmann in Berlin, on the radioactive substances produced when uranium was bombarded with neutrons. I read avidly the papers from the Berlin school on the so-called transuranium elements, which were apparently produced in these neutron reactions with uranium, and in fact fancied myself as a sort of expert on the chemical properties of these "new elements." For example, I gave a seminar in the College of Chemistry in 1936, in which I described very completely the chemical properties of these transuranium elements, basing my description on the work of Hahn and his co-workers.

During the following years I continued to read all the articles in this field and was particularly interested in the work on the neutron irradiation of uranium carried on by my colleagues at the Radiation Laboratory at Berkeley.

I first heard of the correct interpretation for these radio-activities at a seminar in the Department of Physics at Berkeley on a Monday night in January 1939. The information had come through by word of mouth that Hahn and Strassmann in Germany had identified some of these radioactivities as isotopes of barium and lanthanum, and that what actually happened upon the bombardment of uranium with neutrons was the splitting of the uranium nucleus into two approximately equal-sized fragments.

I cannot possibly describe either the excitement that this produced in me or the chagrin I felt in realizing that I had failed to recognize this possibility myself on the basis of all the information available to me, information which I had studied so assiduously for a number of years. After the seminar was over I walked the streets of Berkeley for hours turning over and over in my mind the import of this news from Hahn's laboratory. I was in a combined state of exhilaration because of the beauty of Hahn's and Strassmann's discovery and disappointment because of my stupidity in not having recognized, myself, the fission interpretation as the obvious explanation of the wealth of experimental evidence available to scientists throughout the world.

The impact of Hahn's discovery is a story known the world over. It led to the first observation of the practical nuclear-fission chain reaction by Enrico Fermi and co-workers at the University of Chicago in December 1942.

During that time the world was at war, and as many scientists at work with the atom had speculated that a great explosive force might result from the sudden release of nuclear energy, most of the work on fission was marshaled toward the production of a nuclear weapon—an atomic bomb. The story of the massive scientific and technological effort in the United States to produce such a weapon has been well documented. Some of the world's leading scientists—Fermi, Compton, Oppenheimer, Bush, Conant, Lawrence, Szilard, Wigner, Rabi, Urey, and many others—were recruited to work on various phases of the then highly secret "Manhattan Project," an effort which after three years of work resulted in the successful production of fission weapons.

Even after World War Two was dramatically ended by the use of nuclear weapons, much secrecy concerning the atom still prevailed. But the scientists who had worked on the weapons now turned their attention and efforts to seeking international control of this new force and pursuing its application for civilian uses. It was obvious that wartime atomic developments could not be long kept under lock and key. Furthermore, it was important that the beneficial uses of so powerful and versatile a force, developed through the efforts of scientists of many nationalities, be fully explored and made available to all nations.

Many who worked with nuclear energy had foreseen ways in which the new force could be adapted to peaceful and productive uses. Foremost among these was the use of the heat of nuclear fission to generate electricity. The large plutonium-producing reactors at Hanford, Washington, had produced enough heat in their cooling water to make many believe that such heat energy could eventually be harnessed for that purpose. But much work would have to be done before this could be accomplished, and even the most optimistic of us thought that the economic production of electricity through nuclear power was perhaps decades away.

However, several countries—notably the United States, Great Britain, Canada, France, and the Soviet Union—recognized the future potential of nuclear power and, almost simultaneously, began efforts toward its development.

If the following brief summary of nuclear power history seems to emphasize developments in the United States, it is only because I am most familiar with the nuclear power program in this country. Important progress in this field has been made by many countries, and there has been a gratifying amount of international cooperation in the sharing of technical information concerning reactor development as well as other nuclear research. In fact, I know of no other area of science and technology which has benefited from international cooperation to the extent that nuclear energy has. In this respect it is indeed unique.

Many problems beset early efforts in the United States to develop nuclear power. There was an initial shortage of materials. High-grade reserves of uranium ore had not yet been discovered in the United States. Most uranium ore came from the Belgian Congo and Canada. With a shortage of materials and a somewhat reserved attitude on the part of the scientific community concerning the future of nuclear power, the United States Atomic Energy Commission, which had been established by an Act of Congress in 1946, formulated its first reactor development plan in 1948. Instead of seeking to give a simple demonstration of nuclear power, the plan first emphasized its technical feasibility. Second, because of the shortage of fissionable material, the plan gave priority to the design of a "breeder" reactor. It was believed that such a reactor, while generating power, could produce more fissionable material than it would consume by converting the nonfissionable isotope uranium-238 to the fissionable material plutonium-239. The possibility of such a conversion of material by neutron capture during a chain reaction had been evident since Fermi's earliest work with the fission chain reaction.

The Commission authorized work on two breeder reactors, a "fast" breeder and one of intermediate neutron energies. While the intermediate-breeder concept was created by a group of General Electric scientists led by Harvey Brooks, the concept of the fast breeder was primarily that of Walter H. Zinn, one of Fermi's wartime assistants who in 1946 had become director of the Argonne National Laboratory—the laboratory which in some respects was to become heir to Fermi's initial reactor work under the stands at Stagg Field at the University of Chicago. The intermediate power breeder reactor proposed was never built, but the fast reactor concept was pursued and today its economical development represents one of the most important goals for the use of nuclear power.

The first useful amount of electricity generated from nuclear heat was produced on December 20, 1951, by the Experimental Breeder Reactor No. 1 developed by the Argonne National Laboratory. This historic event took place at the National Reactor Testing Station in Idaho. Four years later, on July 17, 1955, a boiling-water reactor known as Borax-III supplied for a short period of time all the electricity needed by the nearby small city of Arco, Idaho. Also developed at the National Reactor Testing Station in Idaho was a materials testing reactor which achieved criticality in 1952. These facilities were to play an important role in the development of many future power reactors.

However, these early developments were only some of the landmarks in the nuclear power programs which were to be developed throughout the United States and Europe. There are a number of other landmarks of importance. In the summer of 1947 British scientists had built a research reactor at Harwell. They had also designed Britain's first major experimental reactor, BEPO, which served as a prototype for several gas-cooled power reactors. The French operated their first experimental reactor in 1948 and began planning larger ones in 1952. By 1954 the Russians had put into operation a small power demonstration reactor at a new research center at Obninsk. This reactor, designated the AM-1, was the first to achieve a record of continuous production of electricity.

Major impetus to the development of civilian nuclear power, particularly in the United States, was given on December 8, 1953, when President Eisenhower, before the General Assembly of the United Nations, offered a proposal for developing the peaceful uses of atomic energy. The following year an extensive revision by Congress in the United States Atomic Energy Act permitted private industrial companies for the first time to own nuclear reactors. The new legislation also gave the government authority to provide funds and technical assistance to nongovernment reactor projects and to exchange technical data and negotiate cooperative agreements for reactor development with other nations.

In the ensuing years the development of power reactors surged ahead both in the United States and abroad. By this time the prospect of an abundance of uranium ore, resulting from the discovery of vast deposits in the United States, had lessened the immediate emphasis on breeder technology and allowed for the development of other types of reactors to test the basic designs which were under study. These included a pressurized water reactor to be built at Shippingport, Pennsylvania; a sodium-graphite reactor in Southern California; a new experimental breeder reactor using a sodium coolant; and the homogeneous reactor experiment number 2, a greatly improved version of the type which had been conceived and built at Oak Ridge National Laboratory by Alvin M. Weinberg and his associates. The Shippingport reactor was an outgrowth of the work of Hyman Rickover, who as a Navy captain had pioneered the development of pressurized water reactors to propel submarines.

In addition, industrial firms, in cooperation with the government, undertook the construction of four large-scale prototype reactors; a pressurized-water plant at Rowe, Massachusetts; a boiling-water reactor at Morris, Illinois; a sodium-cooled, graphite-moderated reactor at Hallam, Nebraska; and a sodium-cooled fast breeder constructed outside Detroit, Michigan, and named for Enrico Fermi. Later, other prototype reactors were built.

In Great Britain reactor development emphasized gas-cooled technology. In May 1956 the British completed their first power reactor at Calder Hall. Others of the same type, using natural uranium as fuel, graphite as moderator, and carbon-dioxide gas as coolant, were planned for construction in Scotland, as was the Dounreay reactor, a liquid metal-cooled fast breeder.

The development of power reactors in France followed a somewhat similar course. The construction of three natural uranium, graphite-moderated, and gas-cooled reactors was begun in Marcoule in May 1954. As these reactors were designed primarily to produce plutonium, their electrical power output was low, but subsequent reactors constructed at Marcoule were planned to produce more power. In 1957 the French constructed near Chinon their first reactor for power production alone.

Early power reactor development in the Soviet Union emphasized water-cooled systems. By 1954 the Russians were operating a small pressurized-water, graphite-moderated reactor at Obninsk and had announced plans for larger plants to be built at Beloyarsk, New Melekess, and Novovoronezh. These were to include boiling-water and pressurized-water reactors.

Although there was much international enthusiasm during the early 1950s over the prospects of nuclear power, progress was slow. The First International Conference on the Peaceful Uses of Atomic Energy, held in Geneva in 1955, was highly successful and reflected much optimism, but by 1958, the time of the Second Conference, considerable skepticism had developed over the future of this new source of energy.

In 1959, however, the U.S. Atomic Energy Commission announced a new power reactor program emphasizing the need to reduce the cost of nuclear power. The hope was that by developing the economic advantages of relatively larger plants nuclear energy would be able to compete with fossil fuels in areas where power costs were high because of the distance from sources of conventional fuels.

About this time two water-cooled nuclear plants previously mentioned were completed. The Dresden Nuclear Power Station at Morris, Illinois, started up in 1959, and the Yankee Nuclear Power Station, at Rowe, Massachusetts, went "on the line" in 1960. Improvements in design and greater operating experience also helped to exceed expected electrical outputs and reduce fuel and plant costs.

In a report to the President in 1962 on the status and prospects of nuclear power, the AEC, besides outlining future objectives, stated the firm conviction that "the use of nuclear energy for electrical power . . . is technically feasible and economically reasonable." On December 12, 1963, the Jersey Central Power and Light Company announced its decision, based solely on an economic evaluation, to build a water-cooled nuclear power plant at Oyster Creek, New Jersey. This announcement revitalized the interest of private industry and electric utilities in the use of nuclear power, and since then many other major American utilities have committed themselves to the construction of large water-cooled nuclear plants. In some cases the successful operation of a nuclear power plant already supplying electric power has prompted the construction of a second and even a third nuclear plant at the same location.

Interest in nuclear power has also increased in other countries. New reactors are being constructed in Great Britain, France, Germany, Italy, Sweden, Russia, and Switzerland, and reactors have been built in India and Japan. Particularly successful has been Great Britain's continuing development of advanced gas-cooled reactor technology.

The world-wide increase in demand for electrical power, accelerated by increasing industrialization in the developed countries and the new power needs of the emerging nations, is likely to result in expanding use of nuclear energy. In 1955 installed nuclear power capacity was 5 megawatts; in 1958 it was 185; in 1964, 5000. Present predictions are that by 1970 it will be 25,000 megawatts, by 1980 possibly 250,000, and that by the year 2000 one-half of the world's electricity will be generated by nuclear power.

Another potential application of nuclear power is that of large-scale dual-purpose plants for desalting seawater as well as producing electrical power. There is considerable international interest in such plants.

Now that certain types of light-water reactors are being built in the United States by private industry, the government is focusing its attention on the development of advanced converters and breeders, in which the nonfissionable but fertile isotopes uranium-238 and thorium-232 can be transformed into the fissionable isotopes plutonium-239 and uranium-233 respectively. These new fuels can be created at the same time that the reactor is producing electricity. The advanced converter produces almost as much fuel as it consumes; the breeder is capable of producing more new fuel than it burns. The conversion of uranium-238 into plutonium-239 creates an almost inexhaustible source of nuclear power. Similarly, large supplies of thorium can be made available as nuclear fuel by intermediate conversion to fissionable uranium-233.

Today scientists in many countries are also working toward the control of thermonuclear fusion, which is believed to be feasible, although problems have to be solved before it can be accomplished. If controlled fusion is made practical, enormous amounts of power can be produced by using the heavy hydrogen atoms found in common sea water as nuclear fuel.

The production of electricity is perhaps the most practical use of atomic energy today, but nuclear fission also provides power of other kinds. Nuclear propulsion for ships and submarines, first used for naval vessels, has been proved reliable and advantageous, and interest in using it for commercial vessels is developing. The USSR has been operating the nuclear ice-breaker *Lenin* for several years. The United States nuclear-powered cargo-passenger ship, the N.S. *Savannah*, which has traveled over 90,000 miles and visited some forty foreign and domestic ports during its demonstration voyages, has now been put into regular commercial service. The construction of other nuclear ships for the merchant marine has been proposed. Nuclear-powered merchant ships are also being planned and constructed by Japan and Germany. Fittingly enough, Germany's first nuclear vessel, launched in June 1964, was christened the *Otto Hahn*.

The space program will also use nuclear power in a number of ways. Nuclear rocket reactors designed to produce upward of 250,000 pounds of thrust are being developed and tested in the United States for the future purpose of propelling both manned and unmanned flights to the planets. Specially constructed compact nuclear reactors, known in the United States as SNAP devices (the initials SNAP standing for Systems for Nuclear Auxiliary Power), will be used to furnish large amounts of electrical power to space vehicles and for special purposes on land and under the sea.

In addition to these peaceful uses of the atom, nuclear explosives are being developed for use in the rapid and economical construction of canals, harbors, and tunnels. Such explosives are also expected to be useful in mining and in the creation of underground storage areas.

Another development stemming from Hahn's work which has assumed great importance today relates to the uses of radioisotopes—unstable isotopes that emit radiation while decaying. The existence of limited amounts of such material in nature was discovered by Becquerel and the Curies and these natural radioactive substances were further elucidated by Otto Hahn and others. Later it was discovered that artificial radioisotopes of many elements could be made and that the radioactivity of these elements could be useful, particularly because, although they emitted detectable radiation, the radioisotopes behaved chemically in the same way as the stable isotopes.

At first only minute quantities of radioisotopes could be made. A valuable early producer of them was the cyclotron invented by Ernest O. Lawrence. In the 1930s I was fortunate in being among several researchers at the Berkeley campus of the University of California who used Lawrence's cyclotron to bombard various elements in order to create new radioisotopes. We created a variety of useful ones but in relatively small quantities. Hahn's discovery of fission and the resulting development of reactors made possible the production of large quantities of radioisotopes. Now that they can be produced in research reactors or separated from the fission products of power reactors, radioisotopes have become very important in medicine for biological research as well as for the diagnosis and treatment of diseases. The radioisotope has been called the most important scientific tool since the invention of the microscope.

The first reactor-produced radioisotope to be used for medical purposes was carbon-14, made in the "X-10" reactor in Oak Ridge and supplied to the Barnard Cancer Hospital in St. Louis, Missouri, on August 2, 1946. The X-10, which went critical on November 4, 1943, with Fermi and others of his Chicago group present, became the first "wholesale" producer of radioisotopes. The production and use of medical isotopes has now grown to tremendous proportions. They are currently in use in almost every country of the world. In the United States alone more than 4000 hospitals and medical groups use some thirty different radioisotopes in thyroid studies and treatment, metabolic studies, blood cell research, organ function studies, tissue transplant experiments, and cancer diagnosis and therapy.

Radioisotopes are also important in increasing agricultural productivity, which, because of population expansion and the desire for improved living conditions, is one of the most imperative problems facing science today. Calcium-45 and phosphorus-32 are invaluable in studies of plant metabolism and translocation and the uptake of fertilizers. Calcium-45 and iodine-131 have been used in research on soil fertility and to determine the action of growth regulators and herbicides, while carbon-14, sulfur-35, phosphorus-32, calcium-45, and molybdenum-93 and molybdenum-99 have been employed in studies of plant diseases and the effectiveness of fungicides. Radioisotopes have also been used in studies of moisture distribution and root growth, and ever since they were first discovered have been important in research on photosynthesis.

In ways similar to those in which they are employed in research on plant and human physiology and metabolism, radioisotopes are used in tracer studies in animals. The development of better feed and the eradication of certain disease-bearing pests have also been accomplished by the use of radioisotopes, and currently radiation from radioisotopes is being used in grain disinfestation, in producing valuable plant mutations, and in extending the shelf life of perishable foods.

Finally, the radiation emitted from radioisotopes has been valuable in chemical and physical research in a wide variety of industries. It has been useful in developing new and improved products and, in combination with refined detection equipment and automated machinery, has created new standards of quality control in industries as varied as steel, rubber, textiles, paper, and the processing of foods and beverages. Ironically, radiation of the type most hazardous to human beings has been used effectively for human safety in radiographic work to check the structural integrity of the seam welds of boilers or ships' hulls, or to search for flaws in metal castings or pieces of structural steel. A recent survey by the International Atomic Energy Agency reported that twenty-five industrial countries save $300,000,000 to $400,000,000 a year through the use of radio-isotopes.

Direct use of the radiation is not the only feature of radio-isotopes which has been found beneficial. Their decay, over half-lives extending from short times to thousands of years, produces varying degrees of heat. By converting this heat to electricity through the use of such devices as thermocouples, small but long-lived and reliable power units have been developed. Such units, like the compact nuclear reactors mentioned earlier, provide power supplies for communication from self-sustaining remote stations on land, at sea, and in space. An unmanned weather station in the Arctic uses as its power source strontium-90, and orbiting-in-space navigational satellites employ plutonium-238 as a source for electrical power. Other radioisotopes, such as those of curium and cesium, are now being considered as remote power supplies.

At the same time that we continue to expand, develop, and refine the many uses of nuclear energy that have resulted from Otto Hahn's and Fritz Strassmann's historic discovery, we are also continuing, in their spirit of inquiry, to explore the atom and its complex nucleus. Today in the United States there are several large scientific centers which, from secret cloisters of nuclear investigation in World War Two, have developed into national laboratories to which come visitors from all over the world for the exchange of scientific ideas on peacetime uses of atomic energy. In other parts of the world the nuclear sciences are also continuing to develop. Such programs of international cooperation as those of the International Atomic Energy Agency and the International Conferences on the Peaceful Uses of Atomic Energy, held periodically in Geneva, are not only increasing man's knowledge of the nucleus of the atom but finding new ways to harness its enormous and versatile energy.

The International Atomic Energy Agency has played a particularly important role in the peaceful development of nuclear energy around the world, and more support should be given to the work of this little-known organization. Of the greatest significance is its part in preventing the proliferation of nuclear weapons. Because nuclear power reactors produce plutonium in the course of generating electricity and this plutonium can be separated and fashioned into weapons by technically advanced countries, the expansion of nuclear power carries with it a threat of the possible spread of nuclear weapons. While most countries capable of exporting nuclear materials and technology to less-developed nations require some guarantee that this material and knowledge will be used only for peaceful purposes, the IAEA is the only international organization through which safeguard agreements and inspections can be implemented.

It is still possible that through the full cooperation of the more than ninety members of the IAEA the spread of nuclear weapons can be prevented and the peaceful uses of the atom made to prevail. This is a major challenge of our times. Nuclear energy has much to offer to the world—particularly to the newly emerging nations which need power to develop their resources and improve their standard of living. Nuclear power can help to propel these countries into the mainstream of twentieth-century technological development and thus relieve many of the pressures which are the cause of unrest and strife in the world today. In looking back some day over the history of the atom, we may find that this was one of the greatest contributions of nuclear power; I hope so.

The discovery of nuclear fission has truly opened up new horizons for mankind. They are horizons which make it possible for us to expand our search for truth, both inward to the heart of matter and outward to the far reaches of the universe. And they are horizons which offer us both new challenge and great promise.

The work of many men has made possible our entrance into this nuclear age. But among them few have made as momentous a contribution as has Otto Hahn. For his special genius the world of science will be forever grateful.

OTTO HAHN:

A Scientific Autobiography

ONE

Youth and Student Years— 1879 to 1904

I was born March 8, 1879, in Frankfurt am Main, where I attended school until I enrolled at a university. Neither of my parents belonged to an old Frankfurt family; they were considered newcomers. My father, Heinrich Hahn, born in 1845, came from Gundersheim in Rheinhessen. His parents were farmers and grape growers, but as a sideline were glaziers, even making the window frames into which they put the panes of glass. My mother was also born in 1845. Her family had originally lived in a city in northern Germany; the men were merchants, with a few pastors and other "learned men."

Even as a small boy, my father had no taste for farming. He had several brothers, one older and two younger, and since the older brother particularly liked living in the country, he was the one who took over the farm and shop in Gundersheim. For his *Wanderschaft*, the prescribed year of "wandering," my father became a glazier's helper. According to the standards of the time he was far better off than others in his position, since he knew that his parents could support him; still it was his ambition to stand on his own feet. During his *Wanderschaft*, which ranged from North Germany to Switzerland, he learned what the life of young artisans was like under the customary conditions of walking from township to township and working whenever opportunity offered. He later told us children many interesting stories about places and people he had seen.

In 1866, at the age of twenty-one, with apprenticeship and *Wanderschaft* behind him, he came to Frankfurt and found employment with a master glazier, Herr Schön, in the Bockgasse on the Liebfrauenberg. Though he thought of himself as "settled," dramatic days followed when the Prussians marched into the old Free City and annexed it into the Kingdom of Prussia.

In the old section of the city, he met his wife to be, whose maiden name was Charlotte Giese. She was a widow, with one son, Karl, and lived nearby with her mother, also a widow. The two women served lunches to educated young office workers, many of them Jewish. This training made my mother an excellent cook, so good that everybody remarked on it later in her life. My father married the young widow in 1875, when they were both thirty years of age. They had three sons: Heiner, born in 1876; Julius, 1877; and me, 1879. Our half-brother Karl was later legally adopted, and assumed the family name of Hahn.

A few years later my father bought Schön's shop and expanded the originally small enterprise by adding a workshop for picture and mirror framing, and finally even a gilding shop. My father, from being an artisan, became a businessman; helpers trained in glazing, woodworking, and so forth, were hired. Because both my parents were honest, diligent, and interested in continuous self-education, the family soon moved into the upper middle class.

Of course the speedy expansion of the small shop into a

3

large and well-known enterprise was also favored by political events. Frankfurt's annexation by Prussia, followed by Prussia's success in the Franco-Prussian war of 1870–71, caused a rapid expansion of the city which expressed itself mainly in a veritable storm of house building. In those days everybody worked far into the night, and every competent and diligent artisan earned enough to be able to buy real estate.

Their financial success enabled my parents to give up the small and cramped apartment in Bockgasse where I was born and buy an old house, at No. 21 Tönges Lane, in which shops and living quarters were combined. We moved when I was only one or two years old, and I remember my birthplace in the Bock-gasse only from later visits. That first home must have been cramped indeed. We four children slept in a windowless alcove; the staircase was of the spiral type, made of wood; its "handrail" was a rope. My father's workshop was in the basement. The new home in Tönges Lane was much larger. Living quarters were on the third floor, and we boys slept on the fourth, which was a high-ceilinged attic with slanting windows. Whether there was any heating equipment up there is something I don't remember. In any event it never seemed cold, although I do remember that we were given hot water for melting the ice in our washbowls in winter.

The upbringing of the three younger brothers was entirely in the hands of the oldest, Karl. He developed pedagogical talents early in life. He was strict and easily annoyed and we stood in awe of him. We had promised never to play with the boys of Steingasse on the other side of the house, because their background was inferior to our own, and we kept this promise conscientiously. Karl was something special in our eyes, largely because he went to the Municipal High School (incidentally, an excellent one) where Greek and Latin were taught. Karl became

4

a teacher of Greek and Latin himself; he taught for decades at the Goethe High School in Frankfurt am Main. We three younger boys went to the Klinger High School, where the entrance examinations and requirements were less severe. Heiner and Julius both were graduated at the age of fifteen with the "One-Year Privilege" (an examination cutting the two years of compulsory military service to just one) and went to work in Father's business. Heiner, a diligent pupil, was usually at the head of his class; Julius was equally intelligent, but his inclinations were artistic.

Heiner and Julius received a fine general education. They went to Paris and to London and saw something of the world, even though they had to live quite frugally while they were away from home. Heiner took over Father's business, which continued to grow. It is still a thriving enterprise in Frankfurt, called Glasbau Heinrich Hahn and run by Heiner's son Otto. Julius's interest in art led him to found the "Gallery Julius Hahn," located at No. 6 Kaiser Street, which was an important art shop and auction gallery until it was destroyed by aerial bombardment during World War Two.

As for me, my father cherished the hope that I would become an architect. He had an interest in building; he had bought several houses and made alterations in them, and he hoped that I would develop the same interest. Unfortunately I have no talent for drawing and no artistic imagination whatever and was therefore as unfit as possible to be an architect, and this in spite of the fact that in high school I had had the prescribed instruction in drawing. I did reasonably well with geometrical constructions, but to draw anything freehand, such as a stuffed bird or a plant, was impossible for me, and artistic design equally so.

Nobody could say that we three younger brothers were spoiled. Though we didn't like the job, we often had to deliver framed pictures to customers, which we did on Wednesdays, when there was no school, on Saturday afternoons after school, and especially before Christmas when the houseboy simply couldn't handle all the work. We were also taught to be thrifty. I remember that we were given two sugar cubes with our coffee, and if we used only one, we could accumulate the others and Mother would buy them from us at the regular retail price.

Until I was fourteen, I was a sickly child; I managed to survive asthma, angina, diphtheria, and even a rather severe case of pneumonia. Mother was untiring in her nursing; she also called in Catholic sisters to help her and never ceased to admire their pious devotion to their duties. As soon as I passed my four-teenth year I became healthy and have never been seriously ill since. At school I was an adequate but never an outstanding pupil. I remember that in the sixth grade I jumped from eight-eenth place (which was my rank in primary school) to third place, mainly because I learned my first foreign language, French, quickly and pronounced it well. But I remained in third, fourth, or fifth place and never made first place as Heiner did.

I became interested in chemistry when I was fifteen; a friend and I dabbled in chemical "experiments" in our "wash kitchen," as the laundry room was normally called in Germany. My interest grew more serious a year or two later, and when I was in the highest grade of school I attended an evening course on "Organic Dyestuffs" given at the Physical Society (the fore-runner of Frankfurt University) by Professor Martin Freund. (Students in the highest high-school classes were admitted to popular lectures for adults.) Finally I asked my father whether I could study chemistry instead of architecture, and he agreed to the change.

On the advice of a friend of the family who was a chemist,

I selected Marburg as my first university. This meant that I would join a student corps; I would have preferred to join a *Burschenschaft,* a fencing corps,[1] but my parents did not approve, and I therefore joined the students' Natural History–Medical Society, which did not have fencing matches. But contrary to the custom of other "scientific societies," the duty of drinking beer and the rituals connected with official beer-drinking were just as strict as those of the color-wearing corps. My society did wear colors later and eventually became a fencing corps.

Our attention to science was not very noticeable. Therefore my student days proceded without worry and with many happy hours. They were so untrammeled because I had no intention of becoming a scientist and assumed that a job in industry required only learning the "major"—in my case, chemistry. If I had been able to foresee the future, I would have paid more attention to my "minors," particularly to physics and mathematics. I did work

[1] *Translator's Note.* The customary term "dueling corps" is a ridiculous mistranslation. The fencing matches were in no sense duels; the practice had nothing to do with dueling. The corps decided how many matches would be fought with other corps and who should fence with whom. A match was called a *Mensur.* The fencers used razor-sharp *epées* with a dull point. Only slashing strokes were permitted, and each fencer's neck was protected by a thick bandage; his temples were similarly protected, and his eyes were shielded by a heavy cast-iron eyeglass frame that was taped to the temples. Only chin, cheeks, and nose were exposed. The match was decided by a cut more than 1½ inches in length. Outcries were forbidden, as was any motion of the feet during the match. A surgeon was present, and a student who had been wounded could choose to have the wound stitched up so that it would, or would not, leave a scar, called a *Schmiss.* No anesthetics were used in the process. The idea that these matches were duels may have been encouraged by the custom of the challenger's "insulting" the other—the normal insult being to walk up to him in a tavern and say, "Your beer is stale."

reasonably hard in some of the other "minors"—in mineralogy and especially in philosophy, which was taught by the neo-Kantians Cohen and Natorp. A classmate of mine, Georg Dahmer—who was not a member of my society and did not drink as much—encouraged me by example; he was greatly interested in philosophy.

My third and fourth semesters were spent in Munich, where I took the courses in organic chemistry given by Adolf von Baeyer; physical chemistry, by Professor Muthmann; and special inorganic chemistry, by K. A. Hofmann. But I did not attend regularly; [2] instead I went to lectures on art, history of art, and other subjects of general interest.

For my fifth semester I returned to Marburg. Though I was "active" in my student corps I always did my laboratory work. In accordance with what was then a new rule concerning examinations, I began during the sixth semester to work on my doctorate under Privy Councilor [3] Professor Theodor Zincke; it dealt with bromium derivates of isoeugenol. In the course of the work I found one or two so-called methylen-chinones that were of great interest to the examining professor. In July 1901, at the end of the ninth semester, I received my doctorate *magna cum laude,* and during the summer vacation I prepared my thesis for publication.

When I celebrated the sixtieth jubilee of my doctorate in December 1961, I received the following letter from Professor K. Freudenberg of Heidelberg:

[2] *Translator's Note.* It is not the custom to take attendance records in European universities; both students and professors would find this undignified. Similarly students are not examined until they declare themselves ready for the examination, though in this connection some polite prodding may occur after a time.

[3] *Translator's Note.* Privy Councilor is a civil-service rank, also an honorary title bestowed after a long period of service in any of the professions.

Heidelberg, November 25, 1961

Dear Herr Hahn:

I read in *Angewandte Chemie* [Applied Chemistry] that you
had your sixtieth doctorate jubilee. This is not too exciting
when one goes on in years. But I mention it because I am forever involved with your doctoral thesis, which you and Zincke
published in the *Annals*. Your yellow chinon-methide bromate
is to this day the most typical crystalloid of this group of compounds and we use it all the time for demonstrations, since the
dehydration of coniferyl alcohol, which leads to synthetic lig-
nine, produces chinon-methides at every point, and these are
important intermediate products in this process. As you can
see, you have been useful in organic chemistry as well. . . .

Well, maybe I would have become famous if only I had
stuck to organic chemistry.

On October 1, 1901, I reported as a One-Year Volunteer to
the 81st Infantry Regiment in Frankfurt am Main. Of course I
would have preferred to join the artillery regiment in Frankfurt-
Bockenheim, in which horsemanship was more important than
cannon. But serving in the artillery would have been more expensive for a One-Year Volunteer,[4] and since my older brothers
had all served in the infantry, I could not ask for anything different. At first I found military service very strenuous, but I did
well.

There were four One-Year Volunteers in our company. The
others were a young and handsome merchant's son, Theodor
Reisse, and two Jewish comrades-in-arms, Belmont and Bacharach. Reisse and I were treated with a little more respect than
were Belmont and Bacharach—Reisse because his father was an
officer in the reserve and I because I had a Ph.D. Belmont and

---

[4] *Translator's Note.* It would have been considered strange, for example, if
a One-Year Volunteer in artillery did not own his own horse, or wear a
custom-tailored uniform.

Bacharach were nice people but could not have been called very good soldiers. They didn't try to be, partly because they knew that they would not be promoted. Reisse and I were both promoted to private on April 1, 1902, and to corporal on July 1, and both left the service with the right to apply for a commission; the rank had the nice name of Aspirant for Officer. As such I went through the yearly drill periods, first as corporal and later as vice-sergeant, until I passed the examination for officer in the reserve. I could then have applied for officer's rank, but since I had plans to travel I did not do so. Up to the moment when I declined to apply I had been "Vice-Sergeant Herr Otto Hahn"; after that I was merely Vice-Sergeant Otto Hahn, a neat distinction. My brothers all became officers in the reserve.

All in all, the military period in my life was a physically strenuous but healthy diversion without worries. My studies were finished, and the future was no problem. While I was still in uniform, Professor Zincke informed me that, if I wanted to, I could become his assistant, beginning October 1, 1902. I accepted with pleasure; if one had been Zincke's assistant for two years, one could ask for a recommendation to any of the large chemical companies at Hoechst, Griesheim, or Mainkur (all of which later became part of I. G. Farben). I had no plans for a purely scientific career.

My duties consisted in preparing for the lectures which were given by Professor Zincke every morning from 9 to 10. The preparation of demonstration experiments for the lectures in organic chemistry was a minor chore, but for those in inorganic chemistry it was quite a job. Fortunately my predecessor had left me a notebook in which he described in some detail what experiments were required and how they were to be prepared. Of course something new was added from time to time, but not much. Every morning I arrived at the institute some time before

8 A.M. The Privy Councilor came a few minutes after 8 to make sure that everything was ready for his lecture. Though I was not a very skillful experimenter, everything came off well and Professor Zincke was satisfied.

While I was Zincke's assistant, his friend Professor Roser, who was with the dyestuff works in Hoechst, invited me to visit the plant; evidently they wanted to have a look at a possible future member of their scientific staff.

But things turned out differently. Near the end of my two years at Marburg, Zincke received a visit from Director Fischer of the firm of Kalle & Co. (He was the father of Hans Fischer, who later won a Nobel Prize.) Fischer mentioned that his company wished to engage a young chemist who might sometimes be sent abroad. For this reason it was a condition of employment that an applicant have lived in another country and acquired a reasonable familiarity with the language. Professor Zincke asked me whether I would be interested in such a job; if so, he would advise me to go to England for half a year to learn English. This was up to my parents, of course, since it was not likely that I would earn any money during that time and they would have to support me. They were willing, but Zincke then said that I should not go without having something definite to do in England. He therefore wrote a letter to Sir William Ramsay, the director of the Chemical Institute, University College, London, asking whether he would permit me to work in his Institute. The answer was in the affirmative.

Before leaving for London in September 1904, I made a visit to Kalle & Co. in Biebrich. I was told that they would probably employ me but would defer a definite commitment until my return.

TWO

In London with Sir William Ramsay— Fall 1904 to Summer 1905

Sir William Ramsay was not in England when I arrived, and this provided me a two-week opportunity to see London and its museums far more thoroughly than I would have time to do later.

After Sir William had returned from his trip, another German, Dr. Otto Sackur of Breslau, who also wished to work with him, arrived at University College. Ramsay decided to have us do different things. He handed some minerals to Sackur and suggested that he check them for radioactive elements. Then he asked me whether I wanted to work with radium. I replied that I didn't know anything about radium. Ramsay said that did no harm—I would approach the work without preconceived ideas. He handed me a glass bowl holding about 100 grams of barium chloride and said that this contained radium, probably about 10 milligrams. I was to use Madame Curie's method for separating the radium from the barium; then I was to obtain radium in its pure form and produce a number of organic compounds containing radium for the purpose of determining its atomic weight. Ramsay reasoned that organic compounds which had been nicely crystallized would produce more bulk so that it should be possible to find the atomic weight of radium even though only a small amount of it was available. I did not think about the fact that this might be a hazardous undertaking but began to read up on radium and methods of measuring radio-activity; as I have mentioned, I knew practically nothing. My colleague Sackur, meanwhile, set to work on the analysis of the minerals he had been given.

Some time later Sir William handed Sackur and me two samples containing the "elements" actinium and emanium, about which a controversy was then going on. A. Debierne in France had discovered actinium; its emanation had a characteristically short half-life. Emanium had been found by F. Giesel in Germany; it also produced an emanation with a short half-life. But the chemical characteristics of the two had been described quite differently by Debierne and Giesel. Nobody knew whether they were actually the same substance or whether they were two different elements. Ramsay suggested that a careful comparison of their radioactive characteristics might solve the problem.

We wrapped the preparations in paper, inserted them into a cotton-filled glass tube, and blew air through the tube into a measuring tube. A few seconds after the emanation had been blown into the measuring tube the grounding of its electrometer was interrupted. The pointer of the electrometer jumped, but the jumps diminished as the emanation underwent radioactive decay. After about half a minute the pointer became motionless. Since all this happened quite fast, we marked the position of the pointer on a scale with pencil marks. The timing was provided by a metronome that beat out time intervals of about 1.3

seconds. This simple method enabled us to check on the half-life of the emanation. Very soon we could see that Debierne's actinium and Giesel's emanium produced the same emanation, with a half-life of about 3.9 seconds. Just to be certain we also investigated the "induced activity" produced by the emanation (now known as the active deposit) and found identical values for both substances by this method, too.

We thus proved that the two substances discovered independently by two different researchers were identical. Since Debierne had published his discovery first, Giesel's name emanium had to be dropped in favor of Debierne's name actinium, although Giesel had described the chemical characteristics more accurately.

Radiothorium

After we finished these experiments—they did not take much time—I returned to my original work of separating the radium in the barium-chloride sample. It soon became evident that the radium-enriched preparations must harbor another radioactive substance. The liquids resulting from fractionation, which were supposed to contain radium only, produced two types of emanation. One was the long-lived emanation of radium, but there was also a strongly emanating substance which produced an emanation like that from thorium, with a short half-life. I tried to separate this substance by adding some iron to the solutions that should have been essentially free of radium, obtaining an ammonium precipitate which was investigated more carefully. Soon I learned that this type of fractionation— essentially Madame Curie's method—did not lead anywhere. After I had fractionated my preparations for some time, thorium emanation cropped up again in the solutions so that I was forced to conclude that my attempts at separation had not worked.

Later I succeeded in explaining what had happened. The element which emitted thorium emanation was being constantly produced by the substance thought to be radium. I succeeded in enriching a preparation until it was more than 100,000 times as intensive in its radiation as the same quantity of thorium. The conclusion drawn was that this was a new element, formed by thorium, which apparently did not produce any radiation itself. I called the new element radiothorium. Ramsay was much interested in my results, though he himself was not doing any work on radioactive substances at the moment.

Working at Ramsay's Institute was not exactly simple. I had to have space for my chemical apparatus, and I also needed space for making measurements with the electroscope in order to see how my attempts to enrich a sample with radiothorium were progressing. Ramsay was kind enough to hand me a master key that unlocked not only the doors of the Chemical Institute, but those of all the other Institutes of University College. I succeeded in securing a table in the preparation room of the Physical Institute where I placed my electroscope, but I could not use it during the day, because this room was used for preparing lectures for the students. However, my master key enabled me to enter the Physical Institute at night, and for several months I took all my measurements in the late evening hours, usually between 10:00 and 11:30 P.M.; that was the time when I could work undisturbed.

Near the end of my stay, Ramsay asked me about my future plans. I told him about the prospective job with Kalle & Co. in Biebrich. Ramsay said that I should not go into industry—after all, I *had* discovered a new radioactive element, and I should stay with radioactivity, which was certain to be a field with a great future. I should go to Berlin, where the largest of the German universities was located. There, he said, such a new field would have a chance to develop. I replied that I did not know anybody in Berlin. Ramsay said, "But I do." He was referring to his friend Emil Fischer, the director of the Chemical Institute, and he wrote Fischer as follows:

London, 26 March 1905

Dear Friend:

I should not have put off writing you for so long, but time flies without being noticed, especially if one is busy. Now however I have a reason for writing you, which I shall proceed to explain.

About a year ago I bought 5 hundredweights of a Ceylonese mineral because it was radioactive; after repeated melting with $NaHSO_4$ I had a residue that contained SiO_2, $BaSO_4$, etc. This was melted with Na_2CO_3, the SiO_2 was removed, and then the carbonates were dissolved with HCl. Then it was saturated with H_3S, and much PbS and other sulfides were removed. The radioactive carbonates were precipitated once more and then dissolved in HBr. The first operations were carried out by Dr. Denis; then I handed the carbonates to Dr. Hahn so that he could make bromides and have the $RaBr_2$ crystallize. Beautiful crystals of $BaBr_2$ were obtained, but he noticed that the radioactivity increased, and not only in the less soluble fractions but also in the soluble fractions. To make a long story short, it is sufficient to say that he has succeeded in separating a new body—about 40 milligrams—that produces thorium emanation but is about 250,000 times as radioactive as thorium. During the last few days he has even proved that we are dealing with an emanation and he has succeeded in obtaining a partial separation of the thorium emanation from the new one. Thus we probably have isolated an ingredient of thorium and it is a new body. I was most impressed by the daring, dexterity, and perseverance of Dr. Hahn. Naturally I discussed his problems with him daily, but I feel that my contribution to the work is so minor that it is only just for Hahn to publish it himself. Therefore I have communicated his preliminary report to the Royal Society with his name only; it should appear soon in the *Proceedings* and I'll see to it that they send you an offprint.

Now to business: Hahn has studied in Munich and under Zincke in Marburg. He would like to become a professor and I think it would be good if he could do so with you. Would it be possible for him to work in your laboratory for a few years? He is a nice fellow, humble, completely trustworthy, and very talented; I have come to like him very much. He is a German and wishes to remain one; he is also conversant with all the research methods in the field of radioactivity. Would you suggest that he come to you? I know that you want to make your laboratory as many-sided as possible; would you have a corner for him? I believe that he has enough money to live on for about two years; finally, of course, he will need a paying position, either at a university or in industry. I can recommend him strongly—he is one of the best workers I know.

Emil Fischer, in a kind reply in which he asked me to visit him in his home during the summer holidays of 1905, told me that I could work in his laboratory. I could not be a *Privatdozent*[1] because my specialty was not yet being taught, but he was willing to help me.

At this point I began to feel somewhat unsure. I wrote Fischer that it might be better for me to do some more work in the field of radioactivity first. While Sir William Ramsay had made most important discoveries in the field of the new rare gases, I did not think I could learn much from him about radio-

[1] *Translator's Note.* In the German university system a Privatdozent had to fulfill the academic requirements for a professorship but did not receive a salary. The position was in effect preliminary to that of professor. An assistant to a professor in a German univerity was not the equivalent of assistant professor in an American university: an assistant received a salary, was literally an assistant to one particular professor, and usually had to establish himself as a Privatdozent before he could be considered for a full professorship.

activity. Then I asked my parents whether they were willing to pay my expenses for another stay in another country where I would not have any income. Again they were willing.

The leading personality in the field of research on radioactivity was Professor Ernest Rutherford—later Lord Rutherford of Nelson—who was at McGill University, in Montreal, Canada. I wrote to him, asking whether I might work with him for a winter or so; as proof that I had already done some work in this field I added that, while working in Sir William Ramsay's laboratory, I had discovered the new radioactive element radiothorium. In reply Rutherford told me to come to Montreal; we could discuss the details when I got there.

Looking Back on London

When I look back to my days in London, I must say that I was very fortunate. The fact that the barium salts from which I was to isolate radium happened to have been prepared from minerals containing thorium simply forced me to discover radiothorium. The good impression I made on Ramsay helped to bring about my transition from organic chemistry to radiological research; the whole development also led to the shift from industry to an academic career.

Others who worked in Ramsay's institute as foreign guests were less lucky. Otto Sackur had more general and especially more theoretical knowledge than I, but he could not find a new element in his mineral because it didn't contain one. A Japanese professor named Ogawa had particularly bad luck. He started an investigation in Ramsay's laboratory which made him think that he had actually found a new element, which resembled tin but seemed to be separable from it. Both Ramsay and Ogawa felt so sure about it that Ramsay gave a lecture at the Royal

Society about the new element, which was to have the name "nipponium." But its existence could never be proved.

At that time such mistakes were not so tragic. Before a good model of the atomic nucleus had showed that only ninety-two natural elements were possible, "new elements" were announced from time to time. During my stay in London, Ramsay introduced me to a Professor Baskerville who asked me whether I would be willing to accept a job at his Institute in the United States. Professor Baskerville believed that he had separated thorium into three different elements, which he called berzelium, carolinium, and neothorium. The chemical similarity of the numerous members of the rare earth elements seduced many chemists into looking for similar phenomena with other elements.

Ramsay was a great optimist. Of his beautiful work with the rare gases every word still stands. But in other fields of inorganic chemistry and in the area of radioactivity, he lacked experience that would have enabled him to avoid errors. And in connection with radioactivity especially, there was nobody available with whom he could have had logical discussions.

I almost made a bad mistake myself, since, in spite of diligent reading, I did not know much about the basic facts of radium research. I did my chemical work in the old and somewhat grubby laboratory of the Institute where a number of advanced students were also working. The laboratory had a roof of glass set in rusty iron frames. In order to precipitate my thorium preparations I occasionally used hydrogen sulfide. I noticed that, if I repeated this particular experiment, I often obtained a faint film of precipitation. I told this to Ramsay, who said at once, "That is a new stuff"—he thought that my radiothorium had changed into something else. He suggested sending a short communication to the Royal Society. But I was hesitant and asked him not to do it until I felt more sure. The "new stuff" turned out to be caused by the dust that fell off the rusty iron of the roof!

At the time we did not realize that the amounts of radioactive elements in my preparations were far too small to be weighed by themselves, and of course it was even less possible to weigh their products. The new field of radium research was still "full of memorable items," and most chemists did not yet know what conclusions would have to be drawn from the theory of atomic changes advanced by Rutherford and Frederick Soddy. Hence my decision to try to work with Rutherford.

Sir William Ramsay was a very friendly man with great personal charm. On his invitation I attended the annual social gathering of the Royal Society, known as the "Conversazione." Ladies were invited to this gathering; new discoveries and ideas were discussed, and new equipment was shown. Ramsay suggested that I exhibit my radiothorium, using a small cubicle that could be darkened by a curtain. The effects of the emanation from the radiothorium actually could be observed on a zinc-sulfide screen, but only if the screen was really in the dark and the eyes had had time to become adjusted to the darkness. When one came from the bright light outside into the cubicle that was not really dark one could barely see anything. However, this occasion at least gave me the opportunity of meeting several famous men—Lord Rayleigh, the co-discoverer of argon, Sir William Huggins, and others.

The "Conversazione" may also have been the cause of an item in a London newspaper which was later mailed to me by a friend. It read:

A NEW ELEMENT

Very soon the scientific papers will be all agog with a new discovery which has been added to the many brilliant triumphs

20

of Gower street. Dr. Otto Hahn, who is working at University College, has discovered a new radioactive element, extracted from a mineral from Ceylon, named Thorianite, and possibly, it is conjectured, the substance which renders thorium radioactive. Its activity is at least 250,000 times as great as that of thorium, weight for weight. It gives off a gas (generally called an emanation) identical with the radioactive emanation from thorium. Another theory of deep interest is that it is the possible source of a radioactive element possibly stronger in radioactivity than radium itself, and capable of producing all the curious effects which are known of radium up to the present. The discoverer read a paper on the subject to the Royal Society last week, and this should rank, when published, among the most original of recent contributions to scientific literature.

The scientists of Ramsay's Institute were very kind to their two German guests. Sackur and I were invited not only to the home of Sir William and Lady Ramsay, but to those of most of the others. Professor Baly had founded a small choral society, consisting only of Institute members, and I was permitted to attend and sing old English madrigals with them. On one of these occasions I was introduced to Sir William's daughter (later Lady Tidy).

Since one should not look only at the serious side of life, I shall conclude this account of my London experiences with some amusing incidents, even though they have nothing at all to do with science.

I had a minor adventure in London on the day of my arrival. One of my brothers, who had been in London before me, had written to the owner of the boarding house where he had stayed to say that I was coming. He had also told me which bus to take to get from the railroad station to the boarding house, which was at Regent's Park Road. I found the right bus and since it was a double-decker I climbed up to the top in order to see something of London during the ride. I had money; my parents, in addition to a letter of credit, had supplied me with several golden sovereigns. The fare was twopence. When the conductor came I handed him one of the gold pieces. He looked at it and gave it back to me, saying something I did not understand. Since I had not other English money I handed the gold piece back to him. Again he said something unintelligible to me. I did not know what to do. The other passengers began to stare at me. I was saved by the fact that I was carrying a Baedeker, conspicuous because of its red binding. One of the passengers noticed it and came over to me. He told me in German that the conductors were not permitted to accept gold on the upper deck of the bus because circumstances made it impossible for them to check on the genuineness of the coin by making it ring. He gave me two pennies and I paid my fare.

My English—what there was of it—got me into various kinds of minor trouble. One day I entered a barber shop and said as loftily as possible, "Shave, please." The two words were enough to identify me as German and produce the standard question of German barbers as to whether I wished to be shaved only in the direction of the lay of the beard or also against it, with upstrokes on the cheek.

Another time I went to a stationer's shop which also sold postage stamps. Needing some 2½-penny stamps, I asked for "ten half-past-two-penny stamps." The sales girl laughed and instructed me to ask for "tuppence ha'p'ny" stamps—but since it had amused her so much I occasionally repeated my original request in other stores, in order to amuse other young ladies as well.

But the reaction to my mistakes was not always amusement. Either Lady Ramsay or her daughter saw to it that I was invited to a dance. We danced on a floor that was covered with a nice soft carpet. Just to make conversation I told my partner, "You here in England dance on the carpet. We in our country prefer to dance on the naked bottom." I meant, of course, a bare wooden floor, but the young lady gave me a furious look and left me. Sir William's son was present: I went over to him and told him what had happened. He laughed and explained, but the young lady never looked at me again.

THREE

In Montreal with Ernest Rutherford—
Fall 1905 to Summer 1906

Acting upon Rutherford's invitation, I traveled to America in
September 1905. I landed in New York, where I stayed for two
or three days, and then proceeded to Montreal.

I called to introduce myself to Rutherford, and he showed
me around the Macdonald Physics Building. His own laboratory
and those of most of his co-workers were located in the basement
of the Institute.

The next day Rutherford asked me to tell him about my
"new element." He seemed quite skeptical, but I was able to
convince him that I really had something new, not merely the
short-lived thorium-X which he and Soddy had discovered.
Later, Rutherford admitted that he had not believed in the
existence of radiothorium. His skepticism had been increased
by the judgment of his friend Bertram B. Boltwood of Yale University, who had written him that "Hahn's substance appears to
be a new compound of thorium-X and stupidity." Neither
Rutherford nor Boltwood placed much faith in the radioactivity
discoveries of Ramsay's laboratory.

Boltwood soon accepted radiothorium as a new element, but a controversy arose between us over its half-life. I'm going to report on this briefly, because it led, about a year later, to the discovery of still another radioactive element, mesothorium. My direct measurements of the emission had led me to conclude that radiothorium should have a half-life of about 2 years. Boltwood, on the other hand, had checked a number of thorium compounds that were commercially available and found them very weak compared to minerals containing thorium. Evidently radiothorium, which is mainly responsible for the radiation coming from thorium, formed only about one-half of the total thorium in Boltwood's thorium salts. If the "missing" substance had a half-life of about 2 years, its recurring formation should be detectable electroscopically within a few months. But Boltwood did not find such an increase. He concluded that my determination of the half-life must be wrong; radiothorium seemed to be more stable than that. Since each of us insisted that he was right, Rutherford suggested a conference, which took place soon afterward. In the course of the discussion I told Boltwood that our experimental results might be made to agree if one assumed an unknown radioactive element, with a long half-life, between thorium and radiothorium. If this long-lived unknown element had somehow been separated during the preparation of the thorium salts, the lack of activity of Boltwood's salts could be understood. Boltwood did not object in principle, but he insisted that my attempted explanation was purely hypothetical. Still, we parted friends.

Thorium-C and Radioactinium

Sir William Ramsay had made me a present of the radiothorium which I had separated and somewhat enriched; another present was the preparation containing actinium on which Sackur and I had been working when we proved that Giesel's emanium and Debierne's actinium were identical.

At that time Rutherford was chiefly occupied with the study of alpha particles, especially with determining their charge in comparison to their mass. Particles of mass 2 had a single charge, particles of mass 4 a double charge. Since my radiothorium emitted alpha particles he was greatly interested in it. He suggested that I determine the range of the alpha particles from the radioactive precipitation, and also, if possible, the ranges of alpha particles from radiothorium and thorium-X, the mother substances of the active deposit.

The maximum range of particles from preparations that form only a very thin layer can be determined by the scintillations caused by the impact of alpha particles on a zinc-sulfide screen. If the paths are reasonably parallel, the range is given by the cessation of scintillations as the distance is increased. With this method I could easily determine that the alpha particles coming from the active deposit of thorium were much faster than the fastest then known, which were those emitted by radium-C. They also had a much longer range.

A more precise method for measuring the range of alpha particles was developed by W. H. Bragg and R. O. Kleeman. Using a flat counting condenser, they measured the ionization potential of parallel streams of alpha particles as a function of the distance between the preparation and the condenser. Their experiments showed that each radioactive element emits alpha particles of uniform velocity so that the radiating elements can be identified by the range of the particles.

While tracing the ionization curves for the active precipitate of radiothorium I obtained the unexpected result that instead of just one alpha-emitting substance (then called thorium-B, with a half-life of about 1 hour), there were two, the particles from the second having a range of about 86 millimeters. The active precipitate, which was supposed to contain only the "nonradiating" thorium-A, with a half-life of 10.6 hours, and thorium-B, with an assumed half-life of 55 minutes, evidently contained also a short-lived new element, thorium-C. Attempts to separate it out of the precipitate failed; hence I concluded that its half-life was very short. The substance I then called thorium-C is now designated as thorium-C' and it has a half-life of $3 \cdot 10^{-7}$ seconds!

Since at that time every newly discovered radioactive substance was dubbed an "element," thorium-C was the second "new element" of the thorium series. The experiments concerning the alpha rays were then extended to include radiothorium, thorium-X, and the emanation from thorium, and the results were compared with those obtained by Bragg and Kleeman, who had worked with radium.

In addition to working on the alpha particles emitted by the thorium series, I also experimented with the actinium that had been given to me. And there I had the good luck to discover a new substance that had been overlooked in the work in Rutherford's Institute on the products of the decay of actinium. It was between actinium and actinium-X, completely analogous to the position of radiothorium between thorium and thorium-X. I named the substance radioactinium; it decayed by the emission of alpha particles into the already known actinium-X in 19.5 days. The discovery of radioactinium gave me a small triumph over Rutherford. At first he had been reluctant to accept radiothorium. Now I had discovered something that his chemical collaborator, the young Polish researcher, Godlewski had missed. Though Rutherford was skeptical about radioactinium at first, he was soon convinced of its existence.

As a follow-up to the two detailed reports about the alpha rays of the thorium series, I made a similar report on the alpha emission of the actinium series. The following table, from that report, compares the range of the alpha particles of both series:

Table 1   Penetration of alpha particles from various radioactive substances

Actinium Series		Thorium Series	
	range in millimeters		*range in millimeters*
radioactinium	48	radiothorium	39
actinium-B	55	thorium-B	50
actinium emanation	58	thorium emanation	55
actinium-X	65.5	thorium-X	57
		thorium-C	86

Many years later these "elements" were to be recognized as isotopes. This table, dating from 1906, provides the first hint.

In addition to the research mentioned—part of which was not published until after my return to Germany—I participated in the work in Rutherford's special domain: the electromagnetic and electrostatic measurements of the deflection of alpha rays. Because of the powerful radiothorium I had brought from London, the active precipitate of thorium could be investigated in the same way as that of radium. But in the joint article by Rutherford and Hahn on "The Mass of Alpha Particles from Thorium" (*Philosophical Magazine,* October 1906), my own contribution was really only that of general assistance and the preparation of the active deposit of radiothorium.

Looking Back on Montreal

Since I am probably the oldest living pupil of Rutherford during his Montreal days, I want to add some personal impressions of my stay with him.

I soon felt happily at home with the pleasant atmosphere and the professional spirit in Rutherford's laboratory. He had only a few pupils so that he could devote time to each one of them, and he did so almost every day. All his pupils contributed to the rapid development of the new area of research. Their work was always their own, but Rutherford directed what they were working on. R. K. McClung worked on beta rays. Howard Bronson made precision measurements of the half-lives of active deposits. Bronson once told me that his curves were more precise than the lines on the ruled paper which he used to enter his values—and he then discarded the ruled paper. A. S. Eve investigated the intensity of gamma rays emitted by uranium and probably also by thorium minerals. But the electroscopes that he built in the Institute were not as well insulated as they should have been. He took to building his instruments at home, because the Institute was already so contaminated with radioactivity that instruments for the detection of weak gamma rays did not work well. Nobody at that time was as worried about radioactivity as people are now. Rutherford once helped me with a measuring device that was not behaving properly, and in the process of correcting whatever was wrong, he made the instrument radioactive.

Rutherford's special love was always the alpha particle. (Incidentally I don't recall that Rutherford had a special scientific assistant during my time in Montreal. Not counting the mechanic of the Institute, his only helper was a young technician named Gordon.) Rutherford's instrumentation for measuring the deviation caused by electric and magnetic fields was located in the basement. The first result of his work was evidence that alpha particles had to have the mass of an atom—mass 2 if their charge was equal to that of hydrogen, which is 1, or mass 4 if the charge was twice that of a hydrogen atom. But as early as 1902, in a joint publication, Rutherford and Soddy had stated that helium, of mass 4, was more likely because helium is present in all radioactive materials.

Rutherford then considered trying for an *experimental* proof of the formation of helium from radium. When, during the year 1903, Soddy left Montreal to go to England, he made an agreement with Rutherford on future research projects. Rutherford was to try to prove that radium forms helium, while Soddy was to try to prove that radium is produced by uranium—then an unsolved problem because the long-lived intermediate product ionium had not been discovered.

Such experiments had become possible because a German chemist, Professor Giesel, had made a kind of hobby of the commercial production of radium and could sell radium salts (although not 100-percent pure ones) at the amazingly low price of $2.50 per milligram. A little later the price had to be doubled, and a few years after that the price per milligram jumped to $25.00. But in 1903 Rutherford as well as Sir William Ramsay, could buy radium bromide for £1 per milligram.

Soddy, who was then working with Ramsay, apparently forgot his agreement with Rutherford. Using 20 milligrams of radium bromide, he and Ramsay succeeded in proving spectroscopically that helium is formed during the decay of radium. Rutherford then sent his own radium to Soddy on loan for the purpose of having the discovery verified. But in his heart Rutherford was hurt by Soddy's activities, which broke their agreement.

When I was in Montreal, about two years after this discovery, I noticed that Rutherford had nothing but praise for Soddy's scientific accomplishments but was reticent on the subject of his personality.

He spoke much more freely about Ramsay. Ramsay, after his brilliant work on the rare gases, had not been lucky in his research in connection with radioactivity. This was one reason Rutherford had doubted the discovery of radiothorium in Ramsay's Institute. Rutherford always spoke with the greatest respect about J. J. Thomson and with understandable reverence about the Curies. He was a bit partisan when it came to Henri Becquerel, because he and Becquerel had once been involved in a scientific dispute.

One of Rutherford's close friends was Professor Boltwood, with whom I had the controversy over the half-life of radiothorium; Boltwood was an excellent chemist who later discovered ionium. Among Rutherford's co-workers at the time of my stay in Montreal, A. S. Eve was closest to him. Eve's pretty and charming wife was a sister of Rutherford's former pupil and co-worker, Miss Harriet Brooks. There was a bond of friendship as well as of gratitude between Rutherford and Professor Cox, the director of the Macdonald Physics Building. Cox was a good teacher but not a great researcher. As soon as he recognized the astonishing gifts of his younger colleague Rutherford, he did everything in his power to enable him to carry on his research without the burden of a teaching schedule.

Prior to my arrival Godlewski had been with Rutherford, who valued him highly. In addition to myself, another German, Dr. Max Levin, from Göttingen, was in Montreal at the time. He soon mastered the intricacies of research in radioactivity and later became professor at the University of Göttingen. Unfortunately family reasons caused him to resign in order to succeed

his father as owner and director of a cloth-weaving factory—
decidedly a loss to science.

Compared to what was to come later, our instrumentation
was very simple. Our beta-ray and gamma-ray electroscopes
were made of large sheet-metal cans on which tobacco or coffee
cans were mounted. The insulation of the support for the two
metal foils was sulfur, because amber was not then available in Canada. The evacuation of Rutherford's apparatus for
his alpha-particle experiments was accomplished by means of
a rather ancient Töpler pump; often the precipitate to be investigated had largely decayed before we could produce a suf-
ficiently good vacuum. It was in our favor that this whole area
of research was so new that one could have the pleasures of
discovery even with primitive equipment.

Rutherford was considered everywhere in Montreal as the
unquestioned leader of scientific research. Quite often after a
seminar on a purely chemical theme he would make a few short
remarks because it was expected of him, but then he would
forget what had been under discussion and begin to tell the
assembly in his fascinating manner just what he had recently
done and found out about his beloved alpha particles.

Rutherford's enthusiasm and his restless energy rubbed off
on us all. The resumption of work in the laboratory after supper
was the rule rather than the exception, especially for us Germans, who could not stay in Montreal indefinitely. Quite often
the evening was spent in Rutherford's house where the conversation consisted almost exclusively of shop talk, not always according to the wishes of our hostess, who preferred to play the piano
but could rarely get her husband to listen to her.

When Rutherford laughed he could be heard throughout
the Institute. I remember his amusement in connection with a
publication by the German chemist Professor H. Marckwald,

which ended a long controversy between Marckwald and Madame Curie. The element polonium, discovered by Madame Curie, had also been discovered independently by Marckwald, who had named it radiotellurium. Madame Curie had described her polonium as resembling bismuth, which was not quite correct. From the chemical point of view radiotellurium was the better name. Finally radiotellurium and polonium were proved to be identical, and in spite of better chemical justification the name radiotellurium had to be dropped in favor of the older name polonium. Marckwald accepted this and ended his paper with the well-known lines from *Romeo and Juliet:* "What's in a name? That which we call a rose, by any other name would smell as sweet." When Rutherford read this he was enormously pleased with what he called a beautiful exit line. He went around the Institute declaiming the quotation in his resounding voice, and whenever the name of Marckwald was mentioned later, the Shakespeare quotation was sure to follow. Rutherford's youthful enthusiasm was one of the reasons working with him was so pleasant.

Rutherford was a heavy smoker, switching from pipe to cigarettes and back without much interruption. Smoking was discontinued only when the donor of the Macdonald Physics Building, a very wealthy tobacco dealer, visited the Institute. In Macdonald's presence nobody was permitted to smoke, not even Rutherford. Although Macdonald had grown rich on tobacco, he was a violent enemy of smoking.

Rutherford paid little attention to his appearance. His family was not well off, and he had gone to England from New Zealand on a scholarship. One day the Montreal representative of the British journal *Nature* came to the Institute to have the great scientist photographed for his publication. The picture was taken in the basement where Rutherford's alpha-ray equipment was located. After the first shots had been developed, the photographer was not satisfied with the result. The decor was not good enough for the British readers of the journal, and Rutherford was not even wearing a long-sleeved shirt with cuff-links that would show up. For the second picture I lent Rutherford a pair of my "false cuffs," but the photographer returned yet a third time. The cuffs did not show enough! In the third picture they were quite visible and I had the satisfaction of seeing my false cuffs immortalized in *Nature* in 1906.

For a young German in Montreal more than fifty years ago many things were strange; nothing was quite what his Prussian-German upbringing had led him to expect. The ease of relationships with colleagues of one's own age, and even with older ones, the generous cooperation that overcame minor difficulties, would have been completely impossible in the authoritarian Germany of that time. The most astonishing thing was the city itself, consisting as it does of two sectors, one English-Canadian and one French-Canadian. The border between these two areas was invisible, but it went right through the city. If you took the electric streetcar in the English sector the conductor would say, "Tickets, please." But after a certain undistinguished cross street had been passed, the same conductor would call out, "Les billets, Messieurs, s'il vous plait."

One day the famous French actress Sarah Bernhardt came to Montreal to play the role of Hamlet. In the British sector there was much advertising of this unique opportunity, but in the French-Catholic areas warnings were posted to keep the population from the theater in which an actress performed wearing trousers.

McGill University, of which Rutherford's Macdonald Physics Building was a part, was located in the English sector; the French sector had the Catholic Laval University. There was hardly any communication between the two institutions, but at the same time I never noticed any signs of rivalry or heard of any controversies between them.

Life, at least in the circles that had to do with the university, was quite simple and virtually lacking in alcohol. No drinking was permitted in Rutherford's house, for his wife was strictly opposed to it. Professor Eve, who often invited my friend Max Levin and me to his house, used to obtain a bottle of wine on special occasions—my birthday, for example—to please the two Germans.

Through Rutherford we met Professor Cox, the director of the Macdonald Physics Building. His social life was more varied. A typical social evening at his home in winter began with supper (no alcohol), after which games of some kind were arranged. One of these involved a walk into a carpeted room in which a gas-burning candelabrum provided the illumination. A young man had been detailed to turn the stopcock of the candelabrum when a guest appeared at the door. You then had to scuff across the room in order to accumulate a static charge. When you came to the candelabrum, the young man opened the stopcock again and you had to reignite it by means of the electric spark that jumped from your index finger. This worked only because it was a dry winter. If the winter weather was clear, both ladies and gentlemen, paired by lot, were supplied with snowshoes and sent for a walk. An hour later the guests reassembled at the house and were given hot tea.

In other respects, too, life in Montreal seemed very liberal to me. Several times I was invited to the theater by Professor Cox's young daughter, without her parents, but with their knowledge and agreement.

Life in Montreal at that time was also cheap. My boarding house charged me $5.00 a week for room, breakfast, and dinner.

To this I had to add the daily expense of 25 cents for lunch, which was eaten at the university. Of course we did not get very much to eat in our boarding houses, not even in Max Levin's more expensive one which charged $6.00 per week. We therefore decided to eat really well every Sunday night at the Windsor, the best hotel in Montreal. This cost us a dollar apiece, and with the dinner we drank a bottle or two of "the beer that made Milwaukee famous."

After a few months Levin and I had grown so used to the smaller Canadian meals that we no longer needed the hotel dinner on Sunday evening, but we still wanted our beer. The next Sunday night, when we ordered only beer, the waiter told us that he was not permitted to serve beer without food. When he saw how disappointed we looked, he suggested, "Why don't you have a ham sandwich?" So we ordered one. The waiter picked up a sandwich, slightly yellow with age, from a neighboring table, brought it to us, and said, "Now, what do you want to drink?" A little while later the same "prop" sandwich was transferred to another table.

Such minor evasions of the law were convenient in many respects. The barber was, of course, terribly busy on Saturday afternoons, but on all the other days *we* were busy at the Institute and disliked losing time. When I mentioned this to the barber he suggested that I come on Sunday, before noon. I said that, so far as I knew, all stores had to be closed on Sunday, to which he merely replied that businesses like his also had back doors.

I left Montreal in the summer of 1906, after a wonderful time with beloved colleagues and a great teacher whose friendship was a pleasure and whose zeal for knowledge was communicated to everyone around him.

36

FOUR

Berlin: the Chemical Institute of
the University—1906 to 1912

From Montreal I returned to Germany and the beginning of my scientific career. Having been at the best possible source, I had learned the fundamentals of the new science of radium research rather thoroughly. A few papers that I had written while in Montreal had either been published in scientific journals or were about to be. Nevertheless, I looked with some apprehension at the future. Would I be able to establish myself in the new field in my homeland without Rutherford's superb guidance and without aid from older colleagues?

At least I had a reasonably clear-cut program of work to be done. Not everything was clear in regard to either thorium or radiothorium. Even actinium still offered a field for investigation, especially in regard to its chemical properties.

Since Emil Fischer had promised to accept me even before I went to work with Rutherford, I joined his Chemical Institute at the University of Berlin.

The question of where I could work required some thought. Fischer finally suggested the "wood shop," a big room in the basement of the Institute, containing a planing bench as its principal piece of furniture. No one used the room, and Fischer said that I would be undisturbed there. There was no place for radiation measurements in the laboratories on the upper floors, and besides, since I was working in a field outside the curriculum, I could not be an official assistant.

The planing bench was removed and an ordinary table for note-taking and other paper work moved in, as well as a long, massive oak table for the electroscopes. My experience with Rutherford had taught me to have three different electroscopes built, one each for alpha, beta, and gamma rays. In Montreal we had built our electroscopes with the aid of discarded coffee and tobacco cans and the two strips of aluminum foil had been insulated with sulfur beads. In Berlin the electroscopes were neat brass boxes, and, since amber was available, I used that for insulation. The charging of the aluminum-foil strips was done with sticks of hard rubber, charged by rubbing them against the sleeve of one's suit.

But of course what was important was not the furnishings of the wood shop, but the radioactive elements I wanted to investigate. What was the situation regarding the availability of radioactive substances at that time? Radium could be bought in only one place in the whole world, and that was from the discoverer of emanium, F. Giesel of the Quinine Works of Braunschweig. The first preparation I bought weighed 2 milligrams and the price was 100 marks per milligram. Somewhat later I received a grant that enabled me to buy another 10 milligrams. Thorium and radiothorium were available as compounds with ferric hydroxide; radiothorium was several thousand times as active [1] as thorium. In addition to radium, thorium, and radio-

---

[1] *Translator's Note.* In the German original, the term "active" is consistently used to mean "radioactive."

thorium, I owned a nice preparation of actinium salts, also made by Giesel (his emanium). As I mentioned earlier, this was given to me by Sir William Ramsay after Otto Sackur and I had proved that emanium and actinium were the same element.

"Radiolead" (or radium-D) could be obtained in a very diluted form in lead chloride from pitchblende. It was useful for separating radium-E and radium-F (or polonium); highly active radium-D was then still unknown. Uranium, however, in the form of uranyl nitrate, which was then considered worthless by mine-owners, could be bought easily in any quantity.

The only atomic transformation then known—that of uranium into uranium-X—had been studied carefully by Sir William Crookes, Rutherford, and Soddy. At first nothing very interesting could be told about that; the change came quite a number of years later when the new short-lived "element" uranium-X_2, its isomer uranium-Z, the two isotopes uranium-I and uranium-II, and many other things were discovered.

I mentioned earlier my discussion with Professor Boltwood about the half-life of radiothorium, in the course of which we had not agreed on anything. Now, as a result of this discussion, I intended to check the chemical characteristics of thorium and of radiothorium. I also wanted to find out why Boltwood's radiothorium preparations were weaker than the content of thorium in his minerals indicated. In the course of this work I might also be able to prove or disprove my private hypothesis that there might be an unknown transformation product between thorium and radiothorium. Ramsay had told me that the firm of Dr. Otto Knöfler in Berlin was the largest producer of thorium preparations, and one of the first things I did was to get in touch with this company.

Mesothorium

Because of Ramsay's recommendation, Dr. Knöfler was as helpful as possible. All the preparations I wanted were given to me free of charge. I soon discovered the strange fact that it seemed to be impossible to separate radiothorium and thorium chemically. Even thorium salts that had been purified chemically in various ways showed no separation of the "new element" (the term used at that time) from its mother substance. I also observed something else which became important for the hypothesis of an unknown intermediary substance. I asked for and received a number of preparations that were dated exactly; the company had such dated preparations for the purpose of checking the purity of its products and the reliability of the methods of production. With these dated preparations I could see that the newly prepared salts showed the same degree of activity as the thorium minerals—that is, when the measurements were made on samples containing the same quantity of thorium. As the samples aged, their radioactivity weakened. Preparations that were several years old showed only about half as much activity as freshly prepared salts. Fortunately the company still had a few preparations from its earliest production runs; they were 10 years old or a little older. And these salts again showed a higher activity, though not quite as high as that of freshly prepared salts.

The explanation of these findings was simplicity itself. When thorium is extracted from a mineral, an unknown non-radiating substance, which must be the mother substance of radiothorium, remains with the mineral, while the radiothorium is extracted along with the thorium. Since the half-life of radiothorium is about 2 years, the radioactivity of the mixture declines. But this decline is counteracted by an increase in the number of atoms of radiothorium coming from the unknown mother substance that is constantly being formed by the thorium. Assuming the mother substance to have a longer half-life than radiothorium, one should find that a given preparation reaches its minimum of activity after a few years, then a gradual increase occurs, so that an old thorium salt preparation is nearly as powerful as a fresh sample. In effect, a radioactive balance is established between thorium, the newly formed intermediary substance, and the radiothorium springing from that substance; the subsequent reduction in radioactivity is equivalent to the decay of thorium itself. Since the half-life of thorium amounts to several thousand million years, the decline is very gradual indeed. The controversy with Professor Boltwood about the existence of an intermediate product was now cleared up. Boltwood must have worked with preparations that had an age of about 3 years. The changes in over-all activity at that point are so minor that he could not find them. I gave the name mesothorium to the new substance to be inserted between thorium and radiothorium.

I found very soon that mesothorium is virtually non-radiating, but that it produces a beta-ray-emitting substance with a half-life of 6.2 hours. This I named mesothorium-2. A mesothorium preparation that is several days old is, therefore, a mixture of mesothorium-1 and mesothorium-2 in radioactive equilibrium. When, in the discussions to follow, I speak of mesothorium that is more than a few days old, it should be assumed that I am speaking of the mixture of long-lived "non-radiating" mesothorium-1 and its short-lived beta-ray-emitting product, mesothorium-2.

In order to determine the half-life of mesothorium, preparations of different but precisely known ages were changed into oxides by heating and then measured with an alpha-ray electroscope. In a second set of experiments I did not measure the activity of the solid oxide but that of a precisely known amount of watery solution. This was done by removing the thorium emanation by means of a constant stream of air that was then measured for its content of emanation. The two sets of curves thus obtained were analogous, but the decline of activity was greater in the emanation than in the solid oxides. However, the two curves could be made alike by subtracting an alpha activity of 17 percent from the oxides. The explanation was that not only the radiothorium, but also the thorium, emits alpha rays, and the percentage of alpha rays from thorium proper is the same in all preparations.

When radiothorium was discovered, it was believed to be the source of all the activity of thorium salts; thorium itself was not thought to emit any rays. The two series of experiments just mentioned proved that both thorium and radiothorium emit alpha rays. The curves obtained permitted me to calculate the half-life of mesothorium, and I arrived at a figure of about 5½ years, the same value that was found independently by McCoy and Ross.

After my first report about the "new element" had been published, I received a friendly letter from Professor Boltwood, congratulating me on having been correct in my hypothesis.

It then became important to separate the new product from thorium salts of some age or directly from minerals and to determine its chemical characteristics. It was soon evident that mesothorium, when separated from thorium minerals (for example, monazite sands), precipitated with the alkaline earth metals. Since monazite sands, in addition to their content of 4 to 5 percent of thorium, also contain a small amount (about 0.3 percent) of uranium, the radium formed by uranium decay also became associated with the alkaline earth metals, specifically barium. Concentration of the "new element," therefore, was carried out in the same manner as the extraction of radium from pitchblende.

The question of industrial production had to be considered, because the radiothorium formed by the mesothorium emitted the same three groups of rays as radium. In fact, the penetration of the alpha particles from thorium-C (thorium-C′), which I had discovered in Montreal, was greater than that of the alpha particles from radium-C, and the gamma rays emitted by the active deposit, active precipitate, were at least as penetrating as those from radium preparations. In 1907, when mesothorium was discovered, radium was very expensive but much in demand in hospitals. I made a rough calculation which showed that the firm of Knöfler & Co., considering the thorium production it then had, should be able to produce yearly mesothorium amounting to at least 1 gram or perhaps several grams in activity. In radiation emitted, 1 gram of mesothorium was equal to 1 gram of radium.[2] The company agreed to my suggestion that it produce mesothorium along with thorium and increased its staff by hiring a good chemist, Dr. W. Metzener, who later had his own staff of laboratory technicians of both sexes.

With Dr. Metzener's help I then tried to separate the mesothorium from radium. This attempt was just as unsuccessful as my earlier attempt to separate radiothorium from thorium. We suspected a very strong chemical similarity, such as had been observed with some of the rare earth elements that can be separated from each other only by long series of fractional crystallization under rigid conditions.

[2] *Translator's Note.* The term "1 curie" for the activity of any radioactive element that is equivalent to 1 gram of radium had not then been coined. That happened several years later.

The discovery of mesothorium also furnished the explanation for my discovering radiothorium in the preparation handed to me by Sir William Ramsay. The preparation had been made from a mineral that contained uranium as well as thorium. The barium salt I had been given, which was supposed to contain only radium, a product of uranium decay, had also contained mesothorium, formed by the thorium in the mineral. The mesothorium then formed radiothorium. Every time I fractionated the barium salts for the purpose of enriching them with radium, the small amount of radiothorium that had formed in the meantime was removed. Of course the mesothorium-2 was also removed, and for that reason could not be discovered at the time.

The so-called enrichment of radiothorium in the radium-barium solutions might have been one of the labors of Sisyphus; the quantity that had been removed re-formed itself at an even rate. Of course I could not know that, because the mother substance of radiothorium was still unknown. But I was surprised at the poor results of my attempts at separation. My first report on radiothorium contains the sentence: "It must be recognized that this method of fractionation falls far short of the goal even after very many repetitions."

I resigned myself to the fact that a separation of radium and mesothorium could not be accomplished with known methods. This indicated that the chemical similarity of these two elements was even closer than that among the rare earths. That they might have the same chemical characteristics and belong in the same place in the Periodic Table did not occur to me; nor did this occur to me in the case of the very close "similarity" of thorium and radiothorium.

The monazite sand used for the industrial production of mesothorium also contained some radium. About one-fourth of the gamma rays emitted were due to radium, the other three-fourths to mesothorium and the products of its decay. It took some time to develop methods for the production of mesothorium preparations that were as powerful as pure radium salts. The large-scale work was done at the factory; I checked the radiation intensity in the wood shop of the Chemical Institute.

The first mesothorium preparations, equivalent in radiation to about 400 milligrams of radium (and having a radium content of 25 percent), were fractionated by my co-worker Lise Meitner and myself in a basement room next to the wood shop. We did not use anything to protect ourselves from the radiation and obviously the radiation did not do us any harm, if I discount a small amount of damage to some fingers of my left hand.

The Knöfler company marketed the preparations as a substitute for radium, which was being used more and more in medical practice. At the time 1 milligram of radium commanded a price of 250 to 300 marks.[3] The price of mesothorium of equal activity was about half that, but mesothorium preparations had the drawback of being not quite constant in their activity. Because of the decay of mesothorium into radiothorium, the activity of pure radium-free mesothorium at first increases slowly, reaches a maximum after about 3.2 years, and then declines. When the preparation is 10 years old, the decline corresponds to the half-life of mesothorium. Commercial mesothorium was somewhat more satisfactory because of its 25-percent radium content. Maximum emission takes place at the same time, but the decline occurs more slowly. Preparations 10 years old show an activity equal to fresh preparations, after 20

[3] *Translator's Note.* The exchange rate was then 4.20 marks to the U.S. dollar.

years the activity is one-half of that of fresh mesothorium plus radium, and finally only the radium is left. Before and during World War One mesothorium was a preferred substitute for radium in Germany; the quality of the radiation was the same.

Radiothorium also found many scientific customers as a source for the active deposit thorium-B (plus thorium-C, and so on). Thorium-B could easily be deposited as a layer of infinitesimal thickness on a negatively charged metal foil; it had the convenient half-life of 10.6 hours and the chemical characteristics of lead. For all these reasons it was used in numerous investigations employing the method of radioactive indicators first used by Georg von Hévésy and F. Paneth. Thorium-B also played a role in the method of radioactive "recoil" about which more will be said later.

Before I end the discussion of mesothorium and the mesothorium preparations two other items must be mentioned: (1) the making of high-intensity preparations of radium-free mesothorium, and (2) the production of a small stockpile of thorium that was, for practical purposes, free of radiothorium. Both these preparations became important in the discovery of uranium fission more than thirty years after the first discovery of mesothorium.

As regards the first item, for some purely scientific purposes, mesothorium direct from the minerals—which means that it contains radium—is unsuitable. I pointed this out to the Knöfler company and they saved for me a rather large amount of pure thorium salts (several hundred kilograms). These thorium salts contained thorium and radiothorium; mesothorium and radium had been removed. The thorium in the salts produces mesothorium that is free of radium and after 6 years—the half-life of mesothorium—the salts contain about half the mesothorium they can contain. Therefore, after some time, say a year, one can separate the new mesothorium and concentrate it at will, since there is no radium present. Such preparations were used for various investigations—for example, in the work on beta rays that I did with Lise Meitner, which is discussed later in this chapter. Radium-free mesothorium later served as an indicator for a beta-ray-emitting radium isotope during the final investigations about the forming of barium from uranium, the process of uranium fission.

As for the second item, I decided—soon after I had found that not only radiothorium but also thorium emits alpha particles—that I wanted to have some radioactively pure thorium without radiothorium. One could never tell whether such a pure alpha emitter might not become important. While it is easy to separate mesothorium from thorium, to separate radiothorium from thorium is impossible. The only method of obtaining the desired thorium was simple, if tedious. It consisted of removing the newly formed mesothorium from the thorium at regular intervals. This separation interrupts the production of new radiothorium, and the radiothorium still in the thorium decays. For many years we did this to the same original stock of thorium salts, at first at intervals of several months, later more frequently. The result of this tedious work was a thorium that contained only about 1 percent of radiothorium, so that the emission of beta and gamma rays was reduced to a minimum.

Our diligence was rewarded later. During our experiments in irradiating thorium with neutrons, we used this alpha-ray emitter very successfully. That we could prove thorium fission in spite of the weakness of our neutron sources was due to the constantly purified thorium we had. Otherwise the radiation from thorium-X and its decay products would have masked the radiation from the thorium fission products. Of course, if we had had more powerful neutron sources and had obtained a larger quantity of fission products, the tedious job of purifying the thorium would not have been necessary.

The Mother Substance of Radium

Radium had been discovered by separating it out of uranium-bearing minerals, and since radium in minerals could be found only in association with uranium, the two were promptly assumed to have some genetic connection. Attempts were made to obtain radium from uranium salts that were free of radium, but these attempts did not succeed. A calculation based on the half-life of radium showed that the formation of radium from uranium should be detectable (from the emanation) within a week if the starting quantity was 100 grams of uranium. But Soddy, Boltwood, and others showed, in 1905, that the amount of radium formed was less than one-thousandth of the quantity that had been expected. Between uranium and radium there had to be an unknown intermediate substance, with a long half-life, that was separated from the uranium when the latter was refined from the minerals. The case, therefore, seemed to be quite similar to that of mesothorium. Many hypotheses about the unknown substance existed; even the possibility that radium was formed from actinium was being debated.

Personally I was busy at that time (1907) with mesothorium and its properties. While engaged in this work I accidentally discovered the presence of traces of radium emanation—and therefore of radium—in a fairly large quantity of pure thorium salts. This was strange, since the chemical characteristics are so different that any radium which might have been present in the thorium minerals should have been removed in the process of separating the thorium. I repeated my measurements with preparations of different ages which I obtained from Knöfler. In newly prepared salts weighing 100 grams, only the faintest traces of radium emanation could be detected. But the traces became stronger in salts prepared some time before. There was a direct correlation between the presence of radium emanation and the age of the preparation: the older the salts, the larger the amount of emanation. I then repeated the experiment with recently prepared "radium-free" thorium salts and found the same increase. But no such increase could be found in the filtrates of the thorium preparations. The conclusion to be drawn was obvious: the "pure" thorium salts contained the long-sought mother substance of radium, though only in very small amounts. The monazite sands from which the thorium salts were extracted contained only a very little uranium. Therefore, any portion of the uranium-bearing pitchblende containing thorium must also contain the unknown element. For this reason, I wrote to Austria to ask for a sample of the "hydrate" that was a by-product of the extraction of radium from the uranium-pitchblende of Joachimsthal. But I was too late. Before the sample arrived I received news from the United States in the form of a note by Boltwood in *Nature*. He had done precisely what I had intended to do; he had found the substance associated with thorium in the pitchblende, and he had named the new element ionium.

The "hydrates" resulting from extracting radium from pitchblende contained iron, the rare earth elements, and thorium, and it was not difficult to prove the formation of radium in the thorium-bearing fraction. Ionium, considered the direct mother substance of radium, emitted alpha particles. Its half-life was determined to be 80,000 years; this long half-life explained why, in a solution of uranium that lacked ionium, radium was formed so slowly that it could not be observed at first.

I accepted the proof that traces of ionium in monazite sands could be found in chemically pure thorium as just another demonstration of how similar some elements were to one another—in this case thorium, radiothorium, and ionium. More and more groups with such striking similarities were discovered. I could not separate thorium-X from mesothorium chemically, which also meant that I could not separate thorium-X from radium. In 1909 Strömholm and Svedberg proved the chemical identity of thorium-X and actinium-X. This made a total of *four* elements that could not be separated: radium, mesothorium, thorium-X, and actinium-X.

Today it seems beyond belief that this knowledge did not suggest the existence of isotopes. But Moseley and the concept of atomic number, Rutherford and his model of the atomic nucleus, Fajans, Soddy and Fleck with their rule for radioactive progression were all needed before the idea finally occurred to Soddy. I am sure that he did not have as many failures with separation experiments as I have had, but he had more courage.

Work with Lise Meitner on Beta Rays

During the spring of 1907 I had become a Privatdozent for Chemistry under Emil Fischer at the University of Berlin. The numerous organic chemists in Fischer's Institute did not take my work very seriously; it was strange to them and it had no direct connection with what they considered normal chemistry. In fact, a department head, I was told, had greeted my installation with the remark, "It is incredible what gets to be a Privatdozent these days!"

The physicists were somewhat more friendly, and I regularly attended the "colloquium" of the Institute of Physics under Professor Heinrich Rubens. There, on September 28, 1907, I met a young woman physicist, who had just come to Berlin from Vienna. Her name was Lise Meitner. She was planning to attend the lectures on theoretical physics by Max Planck; she had obtained her doctorate in Vienna under Franz Exner, the subject of her doctoral thesis being "Conduction of Heat in Nonhomogeneous Bodies." She had also published a paper entitled "Some Consequences of Fresnel's Reflex Formulae." Later she had worked in Ludwig Boltzmann's Institute for Theoretical Physics, where she met Boltzmann's assistant Stefan Meyer. Meyer introduced her to the new subject of radium research, and soon afterward she published two papers in this field—"On the Absorption of Alpha and Beta Rays" (1906), and "On the Dispersion of Alpha Rays" (1907).

Finding that Max Planck's lectures did not occupy all her time, Doctor Meitner decided to do some experimental work, and she asked Professor Rubens, the director of the Institute of Physics, to suggest someone with whom she might collaborate. He named several of his younger co-workers, mentioning me especially because I had worked with radioactive substances. That is how she came to work with me. The two years she originally had intended to spend in Berlin stretched into thirty years of collaboration and lasting friendship.

The beginning was difficult for her. Emil Fischer, the director of the Chemical Institute, did not then accept women, but he did make a concession in her favor. With the condition that she was not to enter the laboratories where male students were working, she was permitted to work with me in the wood shop. In 1907 this was a really large concession, especially since our line of work was totally strange to Fischer. During the colloquium that preceded my becoming Privatdozent he contradicted me when I reported on radioactive substances in such small amounts that they could not be weighed but were detected only by their activity. Fischer held the opinion that even the smallest amounts of a substance could be detected by smell; he described his own experiences with cacodyl compounds which have a very pronounced smell. But he soon gave in on "nonweighable" amounts of radioactive substances, and in time he also developed an attitude of fatherly friendship toward Lise Meitner. But the rule that she had to stay in the wood shop (which was later extended to include another basement room) remained in force.

However, it was impossible to carry on chemical research in the wood shop. Luckily Professor Alfred Stock, chief of the inorganic chemistry department of the Chemical Institute, was willing to give me space in one of his two private laboratories. I can still remember the room very clearly. There was a solid work table on a raised platform and next to it a large basin filled with mercury, much used by Stock who worked with various gases. At that time the dangers resulting from mercury vapor were not realized, and I paid as little attention to all that mercury next to me as we did later in the Institute of Physics. The countless little spheres of mercury that rested in the cracks of the old wooden flooring were noted but not removed. Later, however, Professor Stock fell ill with mercury poisoning, and he then devoted all his remaining energy to the battle against carelessness in working with mercury and to that against using mercury in amalgam fillings for teeth.

After Lise Meitner had decided to work with me, we had to plan our activities. Part of her time was taken up by Max Planck's lectures and seminars; part of mine was occupied by radiochemical research. But we both had some free time left. We agreed to carry out experiments on the absorption of the beta rays emitted by radioactive elements. As I have mentioned,

I had samples of almost all the known radioactive elements, and from the long-lived mother substances we could obtain active deposits of radium, radiothorium, and actinium. Soon afterward we were able to purchase a large amount of lead chloride from pitchblende; Professor Giesel gave it to us at a reasonable price. Purified lead chloride was later used to obtain radium-E and polonium.

We began our joint work in October 1907. Our purpose was to compare the absorption (in aluminum) of the beta rays of the newly discovered mesothorium (mesothorium-1 + mesothorium-2) with that of the beta rays of the active deposit of thorium. We then hoped to draw some conclusions about their penetration and their velocity.

H. W. Schmidt had said earlier that uniform beta rays should be absorbed in metals according to some exponential equation and that deviations could be explained by the assumption of different groups of beta rays. W. H. Bragg contradicted Schmidt, declaring that the thickness of the layer formed by the substance to be tested was a most important factor. According to Bragg, no simple absorption law was to be expected if the substance formed a thin layer, because then the beta rays absorbed by the metal target would follow a number of different paths.

We did not restrict our investigation to the beta rays of thorium products but expanded it to other beta-radiating substances at our disposal—uranium + uranium-X, radiolead + radium-E, radium-E alone, and radium. When we summarized our results, we came to the conclusion that there is a simple exponential equation for the absorption of the beta rays of specific radioactive elements in aluminum. True, there was an exception—namely, mesothorium-2—but we felt so certain about the uniformity of the beta rays from uniform elements that we explained the noncompliance of mesothorium-2 (for practical purposes mesothorium-1 hardly radiated at all) by a still not understood complexity in the nature of mesothorium-2.

Our first joint report covered more than twelve pages in the *Physikalische Zeitschrift*, which had an unusually large page size. Evidently we were very diligent in those days. I mention this report, in spite of the fact that later developments proved our conclusions and explanations to have been wrong, because that fact does not mean that the work was useless. It was the foundation for the discovery of other beta-radiating substances; it provided us with a convenient method for the first analysis of radioactive preparations, and it turned out to be the origin of the later important work on beta and gamma rays carried out by Lise Meitner and her pupils.

The work that followed seemed at first to corroborate our ideas about the absorption curve of beta radiation. If the decrease failed to follow the exponential rule, we looked for other yet-unknown radiating substances, finding, for example, actinium-C, which had been overlooked before. Our conviction that every element that emitted beta rays would emit only beta rays of uniform velocity and could thus be identified was, in the last analysis, based on a comparison with alpha rays, which I had studied during my stay with Rutherford in Montreal. I should say a little more about that work.

In 1904 W. H. Bragg and R. O. Kleeman published in the *Philosophical Magazine* a beautiful piece of work in which they proved that the alpha rays emitted by radioactive elements had a range which was characteristic for each element. Following the method of Bragg and Kleeman, I had found a hitherto unknown alpha-radiating element in active deposits of thorium and had called it thorium-C (thorium-C′). Rutherford and I then undertook an investigation into the bending of alpha ra-

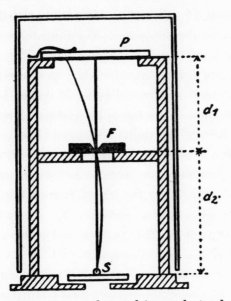

Figure 1. First instrument designed for producing beta-ray spectra.

diation by means of electrical and magnetic fields. We found that the alpha rays from active deposits of thorium-B and thorium-C (thorium-C and thorium-C′) were of uniform strength. Both Lise Meitner and I thought that the results of these researches on alpha rays could be applied to beta radiation. Further investigation of the beta rays from radioactive elements produced some doubtful conclusions, but the year 1910 did bring progress.

Since the facilities in the wood shop were inadequate for the kind of work we had to do, we joined forces with Otto von Baeyer of the University's Institute of Physics. We backtracked to Rutherford's research on the bending of the paths of alpha rays and constructed a piece of apparatus (Figure 1) similar to the one used by Rutherford. The active deposit was collected

55

on a thin wire (S) with a diameter of 0.2 millimeters and a length of about 25 millimeters. This wire rested in a groove at the bottom of the apparatus; 23 millimeters above it a slot (F) was mounted parallel to the groove. The slot, 20 millimeters long and 0.4 millimeters wide, permitted the passage of a narrow beam of the radiation. Mounted 17 millimeters above the slot was a photographic plate (P) with the emission turned toward the radiation source. The bending of the beta rays could be determined from the photographs with the aid of a low-magnification microscope; we measured the distance of the line made by the beta rays from that of the alpha rays which had not been deflected.

The first paper on "Magnetic Line Spectra of Beta Rays" appeared in 1910 under the names of Otto von Baeyer and Otto Hahn (*Physikalische Zeitschrift,* vol. 11, pp. 448–493). We still thought that the experimental results were in agreement with our concept about the homogeneity of the beta rays of each radioactive element. The best picture obtained with the active deposit of thorium showed, just as we had expected, two strong lines, corresponding to the strength of the beta rays from the two beta-radiating substances. But in addition to the strong lines there were weak lines some distance away. These were hard to explain. The results obtained in subsequent experiments with radium-E and mesothorium-2 were even more difficult to account for. Both substances produced weak and washed-out lines, but for mesothorium-2 we also found four strong lines in positions indicating considerable deflection. We could not decide what might have caused these.

During subsequent work with Lise Meitner, the picture quality was steadily improved, due to stronger preparations in thinner layers. The photographs (see the plates entitled "The beta rays of mesothorium-2 and its decay products" in the photographic section following page 72) show the magnetic

56

spectra of the beta rays from mesothorium-2, with its gradual decay and the radiation from the resulting products. The alpha-ray line from radiothorium, weak at first (and undeflected), gradually becomes clearly visible.

Our earlier opinions were beyond salvage now. It was impossible to assume a separate substance for each beta line. Our original explanation of the exponential absorption had been wrong because we had assumed that we had actually measured the absorption. What we had principally measured was the dispersion, and the greater the distance of our preparations from the bottom of the electroscope, the more dispersion had been obtained. In increasing the distance, we had dispersed the weakest beta rays so much that they failed to register, and we had also slowed down the fastest beta rays, so that the average velocity of the nonhomogeneous beta rays remained fairly constant over a short length of time.

In the case of a mixture of two beta-ray emitters with a pronounced difference in average intensity—for example, thorium-B and thorium-C + C'—even the average dispersion was quite different and showed deviations from our exponential law that made it clear that there was more than one kind of radiating substance.

Though our opinion about the "absorption law" had been wrong, the work had considerably improved our techniques. We had learned how to produce different substances in thin layers and also how to handle them, especially those with short half-lives. We had learned to exclude error in establishing the nature of the substances under investigation. And we also found a number of hitherto unknown beta-ray emitters, as the following tabulation shows:

Active deposit of actinium, the beta-ray emitting product actinium-C with a half-life of about 5 minutes; now called actinium-C'', with a half-life of 4.76 minutes.

57

Active deposit of thorium, thorium-D; now called thorium-C″
with a half-life of 3.1 minutes.

Active deposit of radium, radium-C_2, now called radium-C″,
with a half-life of 1.3 minutes.

Fairly soft beta rays from thorium-X.

Very soft beta rays from radium-D.

Fairly soft beta rays from radium.

In a number of reports (mostly published in the *Physikalische Zeitschrift*) we gave the details of the experiments and the finding of these substances. In the case of radium, we could prove that beta rays were not emitted only by the active deposit, as had been thought up to that time; radium itself emits a characteristic type of beta radiation that can be easily absorbed.

Finally, we laid the foundation for Lise Meitner's distinction between secondary beta rays, with their sharp magnetic spectra, and primary beta rays from atomic nuclei which produced the weak, washed-out-looking lines. But this work could not be carried out in the wood shop; it had to wait for the Kaiser Wilhelm Institute for Chemistry that was to come.

Radioactive Recoil

The discovery of the method of radioactive recoil is an example of the way that rather uninteresting minute deviations from the expected results of radioactivity measurements, if investigated carefully, can lead to very interesting insights.

During the years 1907 and 1908 several researchers working with the active deposit of actinium observed a minimal amount of residual activity. Its origin and nature could not be explained at first. In two publications in the *Proceedings* of the Austrian Academy of Science (vol. 114, pp. 1147–58, 1906; and vol. 116, pp. 315–22, 1908), S. Meyer and E. von Schweidler reported on a product of actinium which they had obtained in minute amounts while collecting active deposits from very strong preparations of actinium. If the metal foils that were to be activated were exposed to actinium emanation for several months, a small residual activity was found after the active deposit with its short half-life had disappeared; the strength of this residual activity was about one ten-thousandth of the activity of the active deposit at the beginning.

Meyer and von Schweidler then followed the radioactive decline of the residual activity with the aid of the emission of alpha particles and found a half-life of about 11.8 days, with traces of another activity that diminished more slowly. When they looked for an explanation of their observations they decided that there were several possibilities:

1. One, or maybe several, slowly decaying products of actinium, either actinium-C or C + D, had been found. (The actinium-C with a half-life of 5 minutes, which we later discovered in Berlin, was still unknown at that time.) In this instance the ionizing action of the alpha rays of the new product of actinium must have been astonishingly weak compared with that of other alpha-emitting radioactive elements, namely, only one ten-thousandth of the normal value.
2. What had been found might be a decay product of a still unknown radioactive element which had the same chemical characteristics as actinium, which occurred in the actinium in very small amounts. If this was the case, the residual activity was caused by this impurity and not by actinium.
3. Another possibility was actinium-X, with a half-life of 10.2 days as established by Godlewski, which agreed reasonably

well with the half-life of the hypothetical substance. But Meyer and von Schweidler rejected this third possibility after they had demonstrated that actinium-X does not evaporate even at high temperatures.

By systematically checking this activity, I found that the substance actually was actinium-X, which resembles barium. But how this alkaline earth metal could find its way into the active deposit of the gaseous actinium emanation was beyond understanding, since actinium-X comes earlier in the chain of decay products than the emanation does. Increasing the temperature did not increase the yield, which was minimal and hard to detect, but if the preparation formed a very thin layer, the yield was slightly higher. Just as in collecting active deposit on a negatively charged electrode, the residual activity proved stronger on negatively charged electrodes than it was on electrodes without any charge or with a positive charge.

Finally, I compared equally thin layers of radioactinium and actinium-X. Actinium-X did not show any residual activity, but this was clearly present with radioactinium. Hence radioactinium somehow had to be the cause of the residual activity, but an unknown emanation between radioactinium and actinium could not be found.

Then I found the explanation in the alpha radiation of radioactinium. After all, these alpha particles, like those of all other alpha-radiating substances, are ejected from the active atom with a great deal of kinetic energy. The actinium-X atom, at the moment when it is produced by the radioactinium, carries a positive charge and experiences a recoil from the alpha particle of the radioactinium. This recoil frees it from its bonds and it is transported to the negative electrode. This effect is not related to the actinium-X content of the radioactinium; it occurs if actinium-X is entirely lacking.

Rutherford had predicted this effect; now it had been confirmed by actual experiment.

Somewhat inappropriately I titled my report "On a New Phenomenon during Activation with Actinium"; this sounded as if the results applied only to actinium. At the time I was so deeply involved with actinium that I hardly thought about any other element. But Lise Meitner, after reading my manuscript, said immediately, "What you have observed there with actinium and with fairly thick layers of the preparation should be far easier to observe on alpha-emitting active deposits in infinitesimally thin layers."

On January 16, 1909, the manuscript had been sent out for publication. Less than a week later, on January 22, 1909, Lise Meitner and I read to the Physical Society a preliminary report entitled "A New Method for the Production of Radioactive Decay Products; Thorium-D, a Short-Lived Product of Thorium." We reported on the making of radium-B by way of the recoil of the alpha rays of radium-A; we verified the existence of actinium-C (now called actinium-C''), which we had discovered in another manner by the recoil method; and we described a new beta-emitting product thorium-D (now called thorium-C''), which we had found instead of the short-lived alpha emitter that we had expected to find.

We had been looking for such an alpha emitter because in Montreal I had found an unknown alpha emitter of high penetration, and therefore probably of short half-life, in the active deposit of thorium. Though we made our measurements only a few seconds after finishing the recoil experiment, we did not find any alpha activity, but only the new and unexpected beta activity with a half-life of about 3 minutes, the substance we called thorium-D. We could not find the alpha emitter because, as was shown later by others, it has a half-life of only three ten-millionths of a second.

The recoil method continued to be useful and we found in the active deposit of radium the previously unknown short-lived beta-radiating radium-C_2, now known as radium-C''. My first experiments with actinium had been rather complicated; the use of the recoil method in active deposits suggested by Lise Meitner was far more elegant and also proved fruitful. During our early work on the new method we had received some hints about a much weaker recoil with beta rays; many years later Lise Meitner and her pupils investigated this in detail.

Since I am making a historical survey of work done a long time ago, a discussion of the question of who proved the existence of radioactive recoil may be helpful. After I had delivered my address on the recoil of actinium atoms to the German Physical Society, Rutherford, who had, of course, learned about it, wrote me that his collaborator Miss Harriet Brooks, while working with the active deposit of radium, had observed certain phenomena that seemed to indicate a recoil of the damaged nuclei. I was not familiar with her work, but in Rutherford's handbook on radioactivity, published in 1904, in a section headed "Evaporation of the Product Radium-B at Normal Temperatures," there is a sentence hinting at the possibility of a recoil of alpha-radiating radium-C atoms as the explanation of certain incomprehensible results. But the next sentence is: "But according to the observations by Miss Brooks this secondary activity cannot be concentrated on the negative electrode; it shows a regular distribution over all bodies present even in an electrical field." This absolutely contradicted my experiments with actinium. I had found that the recoiling atoms do accumulate in a negatively charged electrical field. As I wrote in the *Physikalische Zeitschrift* in 1909: "If no electrical field is present or if the electrode carries a positive charge, residual activity cannot be observed or is at a minimum." This became even clearer in the investigation of the active deposits undertaken by Lise Meitner and myself, as is shown in the following comparison:

Radium-B from Radium-A by Radioactive Recoil

Electrical field	−220V.	0	+220 V.
Activity found	100	2.06	0.27

Actinium-C from Actinium-B by Radioactive Recoil

Electrical field	−220V.	0	+220 V.
Activity found	100	1.32	not enough to be measured

The comparison value of 100 at the negative end amounts to several percent of the total activity of the active deposit.

The over-all result of this survey is this: Rutherford had thought about the separation of active decay products from alpha-emitting substances at an early date and had considered a few inconsistencies in the behavior of radium-B at normal temperatures to be due to radioactive recoil. But since no difference could be found whether the electrical potential was positive or negative, his unexplained residual activities cannot be explained by radioactive recoil. The experimental proof of its existence was first furnished in the wood shop in Berlin.

In the course of the year 1909 quite a number of researchers published reports on radioactive recoil, with precise figures about yield, energy released, and the mobility of the particles. Lise Meitner and I later used the derivation of thorium-C″ from the active deposit of thorium as a laboratory exercise for students, since it was impressive and not very difficult.

After the discovery of neutrons and of artificially induced

radioactivity, a new kind of recoil phenomenon was demonstrated experimentally by Leo Szilard and J. A. Chalmers. They utilized the recoil experience by the irradiated atom during an n, γ process to separate it from those atoms that had not been hit by a neutron. The recoil is sufficient to break the chemical bond of that atom in the molecule to which it belongs. When ethyl iodide (an organic compound) was irradiated, the gamma recoil freed elementary iodine which was now radioactive. This active iodine could be separated from the compound by shaking it with water, since the organic iodine compound is insoluble in water.

Similar experiments were carried out at the Kaiser Wilhelm Institute for Chemistry. Starting with fairly large amounts of the original compounds, we were able to obtain both sulfur-35 and phosphorus-32 in high concentrations.

The Szilard-Chalmers method of separating radioactive atoms had found widespread application, including industrial use. Because of the availability of very powerful radiation sources, the method led to the production of substances with radioactive tracers. It is also used to synthesize new chemical compounds that could not be made in any other way, because the original organic compound is broken up by the recoil and its parts then form new compounds.

Looking Back Fifty Years

Lise Meitner's career is an interesting illustration of the difficulties which confronted a woman interested in an academic career at the beginning of the twentieth century. Her early schooling was the customary type for a young girl from a middle-class family. Later, with the aid of private tutors, she prepared for the examination (known as the *Abiturium*) which was the requirement for attending a university, and passed *cum laude*. She then studied at the University of Vienna and was, in 1906, the second woman to receive a doctorate in physics from that university. I have already described how she came to work in the wood shop.

Gradually a pleasant circle of friends gathered around her, mainly members of the Institute of Physics—James Franck, Gustav Hertz, Otto von Baeyer, Peter Pringsheim, Erich Regener, Robert Pohl, and Wilhelm Westphal. All of them became well-known physicists; some became famous. Professor Max Planck and his wife both took an interest in Lise Meitner and in time became her close friends; later, in her years of trouble and need, Planck was always her faithful friend and adviser.

In addition to her work in the wood shop and her classes with Planck, Lise Meitner wrote many articles on problems in physics for the *Naturwissenschaftliche Rundschau,* then edited by Professor Sklarek, whom she had known in Vienna. I myself did a great deal of writing about radioactivity and related problems for the *Zeitschrift für Elektrochemie.* Later we both reported new developments for the *Fortschritte der Physik;* she wrote about themes that were closer to physics, while I took those related to chemistry. At that time a researcher could still do this as a sideline—today it would be impossible.

Lise Meitner's contributions to the *Naturwissenschaftliche Rundschau* evidently were very good, for one day the editor of the Brockhaus Encyclopedia wrote to Professor Sklarek to ask for the address of "Herr" Meitner, because he wanted "him" to write an article for the encyclopedia. In his reply Professer Sklarek pointed out that his contributor was female. The encyclopedia editor replied, immediately and heatedly, that he would not think of publishing an article written by a woman!

65

Of course Lise Meitner could not become a Privatdozent; at that time there were no female professors of any rank in Berlin. But in 1912 Planck took the step of making her an "assistant" at the Institute for Theoretical Physics of the University of Berlin. I think she was one of the first female scientific assistants in all Prussia. She retained this position for three years. From July 1915 until the fall of 1917 she served as an X-ray technician in Austrian field hospitals behind the front lines; she had taken a course in roentgenology and human anatomy at the City Hospital at Lichterfelde, a suburb of Berlin.

After World War One women were admitted to academic careers, and Lise Meitner was able to become *Privatdozentin* for Physics at the University of Berlin. The so-called examining colloquium was waived. But to many the concept of a "scientific female" was still somewhat weird. Lise Meitner's first lecture[4] dealt with "Problems of Cosmic Physics," a subject which of course was quite mysterious at the time. A newspaper reporter who attended the lecture apparently did not think this a proper theme for a woman and reported the title as "Problems of Cosmetic Physics."

In time Lise Meitner attained not only the dignity of a German professor but also one of his proverbial attributes, absent-mindedness. At a congress a male colleague greeted her by saying, "We met on an earlier occasion." Not remembering this earlier occasion, she replied in all seriousness, "You probably mistake me for Professor Hahn." Perhaps she considered this possible because we had published so many papers jointly.

But I want to return to the state of affairs in science fifty years ago. Though the theory of radioactive decay, conceived

---

[4] *Translator's Note.* Such first lectures with which a new professor introduced himself (or, in this case, herself) were semipublic affairs, and the lecture was often published.

by Rutherford and by Soddy, was already several years old, knowledge of the new and fundamentally different definition of the atom had not yet penetrated very deeply. The chemists especially could not realize how incredibly small the quantities of radioactive substances were, or that these minute quantities did represent true chemical elements, the chemical characteristics of which could be described. One had to know the laws of radioactive decay to realize that, for example, the substance called uranium-X, which emits beta rays, can be separated from ordinary uranium in a very simple manner, but never in quantities that can be weighed. Nor could the chemists understand that, if it were possible to obtain uranium-X in such amounts, the substance, weight for weight, would radiate more than 10,000 times as strongly as pure radium. They found it difficult to apply the sacred term "chemical element" to these constantly changing substances which existed only in invisible amounts.

During the first few years after the discovery of the emanations from radium, thorium, and actinium, the effects of the emanations were generally referred to as "induced activity." Because of the work of Rutherford and Soddy, "induced activity" was recognized as being physically present. In my early work, I referred to it as the "active deposit," and I still like this term best. But the German translator of Rutherford's textbook used the term "active precipitate," and that became standard in German articles and books.

In the spring of 1907 there was a meeting of the German Bunsen Society in Hamburg, at which the main theme was radioactivity. I had been invited to deliver one of the major lectures and I spoke about the theory and consequences of radioactive decay. A lively debate followed, during which, among others, the well-known physico-chemist Privy Councilor Tammann asked for the floor. He insisted that radium was not an element and tried to advance other explanations for its behavior. I contradicted with some sharpness; after all, I had been with Rutherford, who was the chief source of the new knowledge. During an intermission my friend Max Levin, who had been with me at Rutherford's laboratory, suggested that I should be more circumspect in my debating. He had just over-heard one of the professors present ask another one who the speaker was, and the reply—"Oh, one of those Anglicized Berliners." In democratic Canada it had not been necessary for a young unknown to be "circumspect" with Rutherford. Incidentally, Tammann himself was not at all angry with me.

During the same meeting of the Bunsen Society, F. von Lerch—then in Berlin with Professor Walter Nernst— reported his newly discovered method of depositing radium-C on strips of sheet nickel. He described the incredible sensitivity of radioactive measurements in the following words: "If we distributed one milligram of radium-C among all the people on earth [then about 2 billion], the amount received by each of them would be enough to discharge five electroscopes in a fraction of a second."

Even Nernst was greatly impressed with this example; the offer of the chair of physics at the University of Innsbruck to von Lerch was certainly influenced by his report on the deposition of radium-C on nickel and his proof of the smallness of the quantities that could still be detected.

The Founding of the Kaiser Wilhelm Society

Emil Fischer's condition that Lise Meitner was not to enter the laboratories where the students—all male—were working was rigidly observed. But Fischer soon became interested in our work and helped wherever he could; after a few years he let us have another room in addition to the wood shop, which we readied for chemical work. Including my corner in Professor Alfred Stock's private laboratory, an arrangement which his successor, Professor Franz Fischer, had agreed to continue, our so-called radioactivity group then had three rooms in which to work. I then had two candidates for the doctorate, Ernst Telschow and Martin Rothenbach, working with me, and Lise Meitner was allowed to take part in purely chemical work—for example, in the fractionation of several hundred milligrams of highly active mesothorium salts.

The fractionation of these radioctive salts, without any special safety rules of any kind, evidently did not impair our health except, perhaps, for very minor damage to the fingertips which were most exposed to radiation. To make matters worse, our preparations also contained about 25 percent radium—from the uranium content of the raw material, monazite—so that we must have been inhaling radium emanation all the time.

These valuable substances were not our property, of course, but belonged to the company producing the thorium, which had spent considerable sums on the equipment needed for the first enrichment of the preparations, beginning with several tons of monazite sands. To help the company get started, Fischer, at my suggestion, had obtained for them a grant of 100,000 marks. This money was to be "repaid" by providing to medical institutes a number of preparations equal in radiation to 10 milligrams of radium. At the time, as has been mentioned, the price of radium was between 250 and 300 marks per milligram; the price of mesothorium was about half that amount.

One day Fischer asked me to give some information about the radiation from mesothorium to a professor of medicine at the Charité Hospital, who wanted to test the effect of the radiation on cultures of tuberculosis bacteria. The elderly gentleman received me most cordially and began the conversation by telling me about his earlier experiments with "semithorium." I said humbly that the substance was called mesothorium. He put his hand on my shoulder and said, "Believe me, my young colleague, the name of the substance is semithorium." Remembering the bad impression I had made at the Bunsen Congress in Hamburg, I said no more.

By 1910 our Institute had produced several hundred milligrams (again, as measured by the radiation in comparison to radium) of mesothorium. A sample of 8 milligrams, so designated by the radiation, actually weighed a little more than 2 milligrams; the strength of mesothorium, therefore, was about four times that of pure radium.

In 1911 Kaiser Wilhelm II suggested the founding of the Kaiser Wilhelm Gesellschaft; [5] its first Institute was to be the Kaiser Wilhelm Institute for Chemistry, located in Dahlem, then a suburb of Berlin. Emil Fischer told me that I could have a small independent department for radioactivity in its building, then still to be erected, and Lise Meitner was invited to come with me.

The official opening of the Institute took place on October 23, 1912, in the presence of the emperor. The Kaiser Wilhelm Institute for Physical Chemistry, built for Professor Fritz Haber with a special grant, was opened the same day.

[5] *Translator's Note.* This name, Kaiser Wilhelm Society, was the over-all name of the organization. It consisted of a number of institutes, devoted exclusively to scientific research. In addition to the Institutes for Chemistry and Physical Chemistry there was one for medical research. A Kaiser Wilhelm Institute for Zoology and a Kaiser Wilhelm Observatory were also planned, but World War One stopped the expansion of the Society, which had been planned to contribute to all branches of the natural sciences. Today the Society—since 1946 called the Max Planck Society—has more than forty research Institutes.

Of course there had to be exhibits for the Kaiser on that occasion, and I was asked to demonstrate a few radioactive substances. I used a preparation of mesothorium equivalent in radiation intensity to 300 milligrams of radium neatly mounted on a velvet cushion in a little box, without any lead shielding whatever! I also had an emanating sample of radiothorium that produced in the dark very nice luminous moving shapes on the screen. But there was one entirely unforseen difficulty.

On the day before the opening an adjutant of the Kaiser came in for a final dress rehearsal. When I guided the high-ranking officer into the dark room to show him my radioactive preparations, he declared, "This is out of the question! We can't take His Majesty into a completely dark room!" There was a prolonged discussion; I called Emil Fischer to help me with my arguments. Finally we compromised on a tiny red bulb. But when the Kaiser arrived on the following day, he had no compunctions whatever about entering a dark room, and the demonstrations went off as planned.

Lise Meitner tried to remain in the background, but she could not prevent the officials from presenting her to the Kaiser, who acknowledged the introduction with some friendly remarks.

With the move from the Chemical Institute of the University of Berlin, the first period of my scientific career came to an end. A number of purely chemical investigations had been completed. The joint investigations with Lise Meitner, which could more properly be classified as physics, were still under way and did not reach their full flowering until a later date.

The years at the Chemical Institute, in the wood shop and in Professor Stock's personal laboratory, had been simple ones. In those days the field of radium research was so new that it was easy to get results with primitive means. During the six or seven years at the Chemical Institute we had no assistant, not even a laboratory technician. The two students working for their doctorates who did join us later did not do minor work for us but carried out their own investigations.

Continued investigations in the same rooms might in time have been hampered by residual radioactivity in the rooms themselves; this certainly existed. One cannot crystallize hundreds of milligrams of mesothorium without contaminating the atmosphere with radium. Therefore our move to the new Institute was a stroke of luck. We showed our gratitude by strict attention to safeguards that prevented contamination and advised our later collaborators on how they should work in order to avoid radiation damage to themselves.

The three Hahn brothers in
1885—left to right,
Julius (eight), Heiner (nine), Otto (six)

The father, Heinrich Hahn
(section of an oil painting
by Professor Gudde)

Otto Hahn, 1901

Sir William Ramsay, 1907

Professor Rutherford in his Laboratory, 1906

*Lord Rutherford
of Nelson, 1934*

Otto Hahn, Bertram B. Boltwood, Ernest Rutherford, Otto von Baeyer. Taken at Starnberg, near Munich, 1910, during a visit by Ernest Rutherford to Germany

The Kaiser Wilhelm Institute for Chemistry in Dahlem, 1913

The dedication of the Kaiser Wilhelm Institute for Chemistry, 1912. Center left— Kaiser Wilhelm II; just behind the Kaiser, to the right—His Excellency von Harnack and Professor Emil Fischer

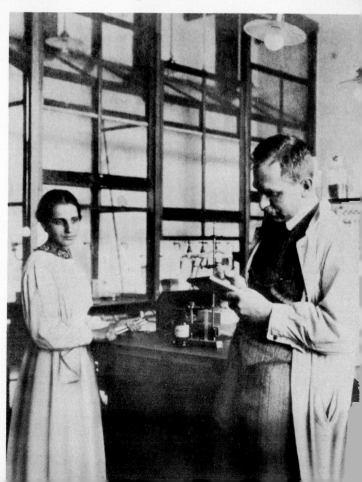

Lise Meitner and Otto Hahn, Dahlem, 1913

*Otto Hahn (with guitar) as
a lieutenant in the German
Army Engineering Corps in World
War One. France, 1916*

*Stefan Meyer,
director of the Radium Institute
in Vienna.
Vienna, about 1920*

Fritz Haber and Albert Einstein. Berlin, about 1910

Standing, left to right—Hugo Grotrian, Wilhelm Westphal, Otto von Baeyer, Peter Pringsheim, Gustav Hertz. Seated, left to right—Hertha Sponer, Albert Einstein, Ingrid Franck, Professor James Franck, Lise Meitner, Fritz Haber, Otto Hahn. Berlin, 1920

Irène and Frédéric Joliot-Curie, about 1930. (Courtesy of Wide World Photos)

The Bunsen Congress on Radioactivity in Münster, 1932. Left to right—Sir James Chadwick, Georg von Hévésy, Mrs. Geiger, Hans Geiger, Lise Meitner, Ernest Rutherford, Otto Hahn, Stefan Meyer, Hans Przibram

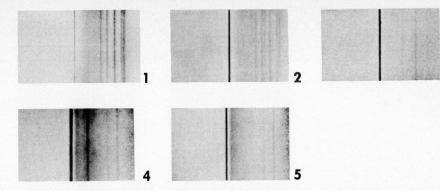

The beta rays of mesothorium-2 and its decay products.
1. Mesothorium-2, freshly prepared. 2. Mesothorium-2, 24 hours old, already showing a faint line from thorium-X. 3. Mesothorium-2, 8 days old. The meso-thorium-2 lines have disappeared, but lines from thorium-X and thorium-A begin to show. 4. Thorium-A + B + C + D. 5. Thorium-B + C + D

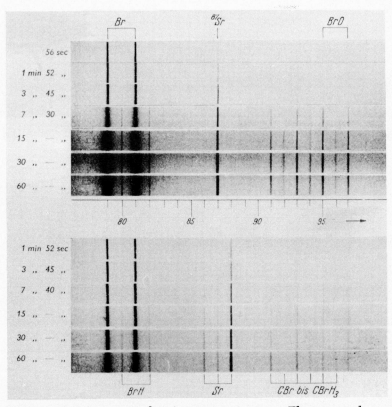

Two composite spectographs of strontium isotopes. The upper photograph com-posed of seven strips of different exposure times (as given at the left of the picture) shows the mass-spectrograph of strontium-87. The lower picture consisting of six strips shows the mixture of the natural isotopes in the same area. The scale between the two spectrographs is a scale of atomic numbers comprising the charge-numbers from 79 to 97

The Kaiser Wilhelm Institute for Chemistry, March 15, 1944

The Institute after reconstruction, 1953

Otto Hönigschmid.
Munich, 1938

Otto Hahn and
Lise Meitner, 1949

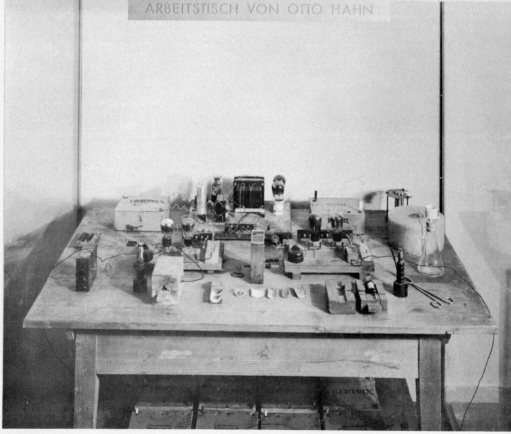

Otto Hahn's work table, now located at the Deutsches Museum, Munich

Otto Hahn and Fritz Strassmann with the bronze plaque commemorating the discovery of uranium fission. The Free University of Berlin, Institute for Organic Chemistry, 1959

BELOW: *Left: Erwin Schrödinger. Alpbach, Austria, 1956. Right: Kasimir Fajans. University of Michigan, 1956*

Enrico Fermi, about 1940. (Courtesy of Brown Brothers)

Professor James Franck.
Chicago, 1952

The Crown Prince of Sweden with Dr. and Mrs. Hahn. Stockholm, 1946

Max Planck congratulates Otto Hahn after his return from Sweden, 1946

Glenn T. Seaborg, 1966

Otto Hahn. Berlin, 1955

FIVE

Scientific Commissions

In addition to the running report on my own experimental work, it seems proper, at this point, to discuss two organizations that were intimately connected with the development of atomic and radioactivity research. Their story provides an instructive picture of changing problems and goals. One of these organizations is the originally German, later international, Commission on Atomic Weights; the other is the Radium Standard Commission which was planned as an international commission from the outset. I belonged to the latter from its inception; for a time I also was a member of the former.

The Commission on Atomic Weights

A Commission on Atomic Weights was already in existence toward the end of the nineteenth century; its function was to sift critically all published work on atomic weights and to compile a table that contained the most reliable values. At first the lightest of all elements, hydrogen, was used as a standard. This was justified as long as the hypothesis of the French-

73

man Prout—that all elements were merely multiples of hydrogen—was still acceptable. After the incorrectness of Prout's hypothesis had been proved experimentally, it became clear that oxygen was a better reference standard.

The German Commission (consisting of W. Ostwald, Landolt, Seubert, and others) circulated an invitation to chemical societies in other countries to found an International Commission on Atomic Weights and suggested at the same time the use of oxygen with an atomic weight of 16 as the basis for an atomic table. The International Commission on Atomic Weights was founded in 1902. It had as members one Englishman (Thorpe), one American (Clarke), and one German (Seubert); later two Frenchmen (Moissan and Urbain) joined the commission. By 1905 chemists of all countries were using atomic weights based on oxygen = 16.

The International Commission issued reports regularly until the year 1916. During the preceding years the determination of atomic weights had been refined to an astonishing degree by T. W. Richards and his pupils. Subsequent development was on a different track. The proof that isotopes were not restricted to naturally radioactive elements but could also be found among rather common chemical elements indicated that "atomic weight" was no longer the unchanging characteristic of an element. Atomic number assumed the dominant place, and atomic weight was recognized as the more or less accidental result of the isotope mixtures of each element.

World War One destroyed the international amity; the International Commission would not accept German members. As a result, another German Commission for Atomic Weights was founded, with Max Bodenstein, Otto Hönigschmid, R. J. Meyer, W. Ostwald, and myself as members. The first report of this new Commission after the end of the war was published in 1921 and mirrored the development that had taken place by appearing in two parts. Part I listed what were now dubbed "practical atomic weights" for chemists. Part II contained the latest results of atomic research and was called: "Table of the Chemical Elements and Kinds of Atoms in the Order of Their Atomic Numbers." These reports were published at intervals until 1931 and indicated the increasing importance of mass-spectroscopic measurements, even for the "practical atomic weights." In both tables oxygen with an atomic weight of 16 was the reference element. But the discovery of the two oxygen isotopes, oxygen-17 and oxygen-18, had caused a change: chemists still considered the mixture of isotopes as oxygen-16, while to the physicist oxygen-16 meant that specific isotope. As a result, chemists and physicists used slightly different tables.

In 1930 the International Chemical Union split its Committee for Chemical Elements into three commissions: (1) an International Commission for Atomic Weights, (2) an International Atom Commission, and (3) a Commission for Radioactivity Standards, which was to be a bridge to the International Radium Standard Commission. At that time German scientists were again accepted as members of the International Commission for Atomic Weights; consequently the German Commission for Atomic Weights was dissolved in 1931.

However, it was not one of the duties of the International Commission on Atomic Weights to keep information on the results of isotope research up to date. I was therefore requested by the German Chemical Society to continue with my isotope reports, which I did until 1938. The tables were based mainly on physical methods, especially mass spectroscopy, and in

75

1940 they had three authors: Flügge, J. Mattauch, and myself. Beginning in 1941, Flügge and Mattauch continued the tables without me. Since the material had grown enormously, they published it in 1942 in book form (*Kernphysikalische Tabellen*, Springer Verlag, Berlin). After twenty years of reporting on atomic weights and isotopes I no longer felt completely competent, so I resigned, but I remained a member of the International Atom Commission (not the one on Atomic Weights) until it, as well as the International Radium Standards Commission, merged into the Joint Commission on Standards, Units, and Constants of Radioactivity of the International Union of Pure and Applied Chemistry, and the equivalent organization of physicists.

Later developments, consisting mainly of the achievement of an unprecedented degree of accuracy in chemical and physical measurements, made it clear that the mixture of isotopes of so-called natural oxygen ruined the concept of an absolute constancy of its atomic weight. The same reasoning applied to most of the other lighter elements. "Natural" oxygen has ceased to be useful as a reference weight for atomic weights.

For years there was discussion about a new standard which could be used by both chemists and physicists. Many suggestions were made, but Mattauch (in 1953) proposed and defended the choice of carbon-12 as a basis. A study commission under his leadership recommended to the International Physical Union (Ottawa, 1960) and the International Chemical Union (Montreal, 1961) that the nucleus of carbon-12 be considered 12 units. The recommendation was accepted and the International Table of Chemical Atomic Weights based on this standard was published for the first time in 1961.

The International Radium
Standard Commission

Because of the rapid development of radium research since the beginning of the twentieth century, and also because of the great importance radium had acquired in medical practice, its price kept rising by large leaps. The development of reliable ways of determining the actual strength of radium-enriched compounds became imperative. Giesel's preparations of radium salts could not yet claim high purity, but the steadily increasing price and the ever-widening use called not only for the establishment of a scale for radioactive strength but also for some official place where such measurements would be made. I was often asked personally, by chemical companies as well as by individual physicians, to assess radioactive compounds, which I tried to do by comparing them with a privately owned radium preparation which I had bought from Giesel.

In September 1910 an International Radium Congress convened in Brussels. It was attended by the most important representatives of radium research, the most notable being Rutherford and Madame Curie. At this congress I met for the first time Madame Curie, André Debierne, and Frederick Soddy; many of the others were already known to me. The congress decided to found an International Radium Standard Commission, with the following experts as members: Madame Curie and A. Debierne of France, E. Rutherford and F. Soddy of England, S. Meyer and E. von Schweidler of Austria, O. Hahn and H. Geitel of Germany, B. B. Boltwood of the United States, and A. S. Eve of Canada. Madame Curie in Paris and the atomic-weight specialist Otto Hönigschmid at the Radium Institute in Vienna were asked to produce samples of pure

77

waterless radium chloride independently and to have them ready for comparison at a later meeting of the commission.

The first official meeting of the commission took place in Paris in March 1912. Madame Curie had one standard preparation ready; Professor Hönigschmid brought three with him. They were compared by means of two different methods of measuring their emission of gamma rays, and all were found to be of the same strength within a few tenths of 1 percent. Madame Curie's preparation, with a radium content of 21.99 milligrams, was declared to be the international radium standard and was deposited at the Bureau des Poids et Mesures [1] in Paris. One of Hönigschmid's preparations, with a radium content of 31.17 milligrams, was deposited in Vienna as another standard. Additional secondary standards, which had been compared with these two official primary standards, were deposited in various places, including the Physikalisch-Technische Reichsanstalt [2] in Berlin.

But the necessity for controllable measurements of intensity was not restricted to radium. Beginning about 1910, mesothorium was increasingly used as a cheaper substitute for radium, especially in Germany, and I found it necessary to begin a thorough investigation of the gamma-ray activity of several radioactive substances. I used pure radium, freshly prepared mesothorium which contained little radiothorium, aged mesothorium that therefore contained more radiothorium, and finally mesothorium that was free of radium. All these preparations were put into small glass tubes, which were then fused shut, and the emission of gamma rays was measured. The meas-

[1] *Translator's Note.* "Bureau of Weights and Measures" (Paris) and "Physical-Technological Bureau of the Realm" (Berlin) are both equivalents of the Bureau of Standards in Washington, D.C.
[2] *See Note 1.*

urements were made through layers of lead of increasing thickness, the thinnest being about 3.3 millimeters and the heaviest 45 millimeters thick. The various preparations could be distinguished by the degree of penetration accomplished by their gamma rays. If all the preparations showed the same degree of gamma-ray emission when measured through a lead sheet 3.3 millimeters thick, after a penetration of lead 45 millimeters thick, the comparison was as follows: radium read 100 (an arbitrary figure set down for purposes of comparison), newly prepared mesothorium 81.4, aged mesothorium 100.2, mesothorium free of radium 73.3, and the active precipitate of radiothorium 134.3. Obviously the absorption curves of gamma-ray emission could therefore be used to distinguish mesothorium and radium.

Ten years later W. Bothe of the Physikalisch-Technische Reichsanstalt extended the gamma-ray-absorption curves to a lead thickness of 110 millimeters. With that thickness of lead freshly prepared mesothorium gave the value of 50 (radium was again considered 100) but radiothorium checked out at 250, a proof of the mighty penetrating power of its gamma rays.

The appearance of mesothorium in medical practice, coupled with the fact that its gamma-ray activity changed with time, indicated that the International Radium Standard Commission had not finished its work when it established standards but would have new problems as time went on.

Some time later the long-lived isotope of element no. 91 (protactinium, which I had discovered in collaboration with Lise Meitner) became available in sufficient quantities for medical use. But since protactinium does not emit penetrating gamma rays, its activity could not be determined by the method of gamma-ray measurement used for radium and mesothorium, and had to be determined by measuring alpha and beta radiation, with attention to the age of the preparation under investigation.

After the discovery of nuclear fission, with the accompanying possibility of making artificial radioactive elements of almost any intensity of radiation, the problems facing the commission multiplied beyond its ability to handle them. For this reason the International Radium Standard Commission was dissolved in 1949, to be succeeded by the Joint Commission of Standards, Units, and Constants of Radioactivity. Those members of the original commission who were still alive became advisory consultants of the new organization.

S I X

At the Kaiser Wilhelm Institute for Chemistry—1913 to 1933: Work with Naturally Radioactive Elements and Isotopes

The years in the wood shop of the Chemical Institute of the University had been busy and successful ones. Lise Meitner and I were taken seriously by the physicists; I have already mentioned the friendly atmosphere among my colleagues, younger ones as well as those of my own age. I also got along well with the chemists—partly, I think, because my very different line of research did not compete with the research done by the many Privatdozents who worked in Fischer's Institute. Still surviving from those days are my friends Burkhard Helferich, Walter Freudenberg, and Otto Warburg. But I was making no progress toward an academic career. The physicists considered me a chemist whose chemical research happened to be checked by means of physical instruments. To the chemists

I was the man who said that he had made his discoveries by means of strips of aluminum foil in primitive electroscopes, and some of whose discoveries could not even be weighed.

Therefore the founding of the Kaiser Wilhelm Society and the building of the Kaiser Wilhelm Institute for Chemistry were lucky circumstances for me, as well as for Lise Meitner, who soon joined me in my department for radioactivity research, though at first as a "guest researcher." The larger departments of the Institutes were headed by Privy Councilor Ernst Beckmann and Professor Richard Willstätter.

The budget of the department for radioactivity research in the new Institute was quite modest in the beginning. It amounted to 2000 marks per year—1000 for supplies and equipment and 1000 for the salary of an assistant. For this post I chose Dr. Martin Rothenbach, who had done his doctoral thesis about the chemical characteristics of actinium under my supervision. (Unfortunately, he was not with me long; he was killed by enemy action in France, October 8, 1914.) My second doctoral candidate in Fischer's Institute, Ernst Telschow, had worked on the radioactive properties of actinium. After he passed his examinations he became an assistant in Fischer's Institute and thereby dropped out of research on radioactivity. Doctor Telschow later became a member of the administration of the Kaiser Wilhelm Society; in 1938 he became its Director General, and after 1945 was one of the two Managing Secretaries of the directorate.

Considering the assistants, technicians, and equipment now required in a comparable laboratory, Lise Meitner and I had not been coddled at Fischer's Institute. Having neither assistants nor laboratory technicians, we had done everything with our own hands, and we were lucky that research work on radium did not then require much equipment. At the Kaiser Wilhelm Institute, although the budget was modest, conditions were now far superior—big beautiful rooms, a large chemical laboratory, a special laboratory for physical measurements, and, most important, a brand-new building without radioactive contamination. To avoid the latter danger as much as possible, I left a large portion of my radioactive preparations at the Chemical Institute of the University, where I still needed them for demonstrations in the course I gave on radioactivity. But at Dahlem it was also much easier to avoid contamination than it had been in the cramped space at Fischer's Institute.

The Activity of Rubidium and of Potassium—and a New Method of Geological Dating

At Fischer's Institute we had worked with all the known radioactive elements that had any connection with uranium and with thorium; in fact, a few of these elements had been discovered there. But two other elements, potassium and rubidium, had previously been found to show radioactivity. Very little was known about either of these beyond the facts that both emitted beta rays and that their radioactivity, compared to that of uranium, was rather weak. The intensity of the radiation from potassium had been estimated to be about one-thousandth of the beta-ray emission of uranium; that of rubidium was slightly more powerful. Of course I was eager to learn more about the activity of these substances, and the uncontaminated rooms of the Kaiser Wilhelm Institute were a suitable place for an investigation of these alkali metals.

I want to discuss this work in some detail because the continuation of these studies led, decades later, to the rubidium-strontium method of dating very old geological formations. I suggested to Martin Rothenbach that he begin a thorough study covering the penetration of the beta rays from potassium and rubidium, comparing the intensity of these rays with that of beta rays from uranium, and investigating the possibility of the existence of an unknown carrier of this beta-ray activity. The comparison with uranium would enable me to make a preliminary guess at the half-life of the radioactive alkali metal.

The comparison involved the activity of very thin layers of the alkali salts with the penetrating rays from uranium-X_2 and the rays from uranium-X_1 which could be easily absorbed. Because the activity of the alkali salts was weak, a large surface was required; the electroscopes had to cover an ionization chamber 30 by 30 centimeters square, with a height of 10 centimeters [about 12 by 12 by 4 inches]. Potassium was not active enough to permit even an approximate comparison with uranium preparations; therefore the subsequent work was essentially restricted to rubidium. It turned out that uranium-X_1 emitted beta rays that had the same power of penetration as the beta rays from rubidium, so that the two could be compared directly. The curve of absorption of the soft beta rays from uranium-X_1 was calculated from the curve obtained with a thin layer of uranium-X_1 and uranium-X_2. The experience with beta rays from various radioactive elements which Lise Meitner and I had gained in the wood shop was useful indeed during this phase of the work.

The main results of our work were these: We found no reason to assume the existence of a rubidium isotope with a comparatively short half-life as the true source of the radio-activity; we established values for the penetrating power of rubidium beta rays and compared them with the values obtainable with uranium-X_1 and with radium; and we estimated the half-life of rubidium. If the radioactivity was calculated under consideration of the different number of atoms per gram of rubidium and per gram of uranium the result was a half-life for rubidium of $2 \cdot 10^{11}$ years. This particular report concluded with a discussion of the possibility of proving experimentally the transformation of rubidium into strontium and the transformation of potassium into calcium. The probability that such a transformation could be proved was somewhat higher for rubidium.

More than twenty years passed before I worked with rubidium again. As before, I was interested in the problem of obtaining measurable amounts of strontium from rubidium, and I tried to find minerals that contained a high percentage of rubidium and were as free of the alkaline earth metals [1] as possible. In 1933, when I was for some months a visiting professor at Cornell University, my attention was called to a mica-like mineral from Manitoba, Canada, which was known to contain a small percentage of rubidium in addition to cesium. Through the good offices of Professor Papish of Cornell I obtained several kilograms of this mineral. A rough calculation showed that, on the assumption of a small percentage of rubidium, the geological age of this mineral should be high enough to extract measurable amounts of strontium that had originally been rubidium. Of course the calculation was made on the assumption that my estimate of the half-life of rubidium, made twenty years earlier, was reasonably correct.

Here was a possibility for a new method of geological dating which should be superior to the customary method based on the transformation of uranium into helium and lead. At an age of 1 billion years or more minerals containing uranium and thorium are no longer pure products. They contain a great deal of lead and a good many cubic centimeters of helium for every gram of uranium. Since some of the helium

[1] *Translator's Note.* These are beryllium, magnesium, calcium, strontium, barium, and radium.

85

is sure to escape from the mineral, the calculated age is always too low; the minerals seem to be younger than they really are. Even calculating only by the lead that has been formed, if the minerals are very old, the results are likely to be correct only for certain selected specimens.

I asked Fritz Strassmann and E. Walling to undertake the difficult work of extracting the strontium from the Canadian mica. An amount of 1012 grams of mica yielded 263.4 milligrams of strontium carbonate, corresponding to 156 milligrams of metallic strontium. Mattauch then carried out an analysis with the mass spectrometer and obtained the surprising result that all the strontium was the same isotope, strontium-87. This proved that it had all been formed by the beta-ray decay of a specific rubidium isotope, rubidium-87. The purity of the isotope also bore witness to the careful work by Strassmann and Walling, who had checked the comparatively large amount of the raw material to be sure that natural strontium was completely absent.

This beautiful result suggested two possibilities. If one accepted the half-life of rubidium (or, more accurately, that of rubidium-87, which comprises 27.8 percent of the mixed natural rubidium) as being correct, the age of the mica could be calculated from the amount of strontium-87 that had been formed. Or, if one knew the geological age of the mineral, the half-life of the beta-emitting rubidium isotope could be calculated. (See the plates entitled "Two composite spectographs of strontium isotopes" in the photographic section following page 72.) By a happy coincidence the age of this mica was well established, because two separate and independent determinations had been made for uranium minerals from the same geological deposit and therefore of the same age. According to J. S. Delury and H. V. Ellsworth (*Report of the Com-*

mittee on the Measurement of Geologic Time, 1932), the age of the uranium minerals was 1975 million years. The rubidium content of the mica—established as 2.6 percent by Strassmann and Walling—and the amount of strontium that would be formed in 2 billion years showed for the rubidium a half-life of $2.3 \cdot 10^{11}$ years, only slightly higher than my original estimate.

During the years that followed my first estimate, other calculations about the half-life of rubidium, leading to somewhat different figures, had been published. Even now the figures given by different researchers still vary within certain limits. For the active isotope the limits are $4 \cdot 10^{10}$ and $6 \cdot 10^{10}$, with a probable mean value of $5 \cdot 10^{10}$ years. Since rubidium-87 accounts for 27.8 percent of the mixed natural element, the half-life of the latter acquires the mean value of $1.8 \cdot 10^{11}$ years, in very nice agreement with the original estimate of $2 \cdot 10^{11}$ years (Hahn and Rothenbach) and $2.3 \cdot 10^{11}$ years (Strassmann and Walling).

Certainly the work of Strassmann, Walling, and Mattauch established experimental proof that the transformation of rubidium into strontium can be used for the determination of the geological age of minerals. The method has the advantage that the mineral itself remains virtually unchanged; neither gaseous helium nor lead is formed in the process. For very old minerals, therefore, the rubidium-strontium method is more reliable than the uranium-lead-helium method. Its disadvantages are the relative rarity of rubidium-containing minerals and the rather tedious chemical analysis for rubidium and strontium.

This new way of establishing geological ages was taken up by others and both simplified and refined. First the chemical analysis was replaced by a spectroscopic analysis, which was superseded by the superior mass-spectroscopic analysis. The latter especially can be used with much smaller mineral samples. With its aid a long list of old minerals from Canada, South Africa, and Sweden could be dated. Even the age of stony meteorites could be determined by this method, using only one gram of meteoritic material with a content of one-millionth of a gram of rubidium. None of this has been my own work; it is mentioned here to show that the idea evolved in the Kaiser Wilhelm Institute for Chemistry was successfully developed as a new method for determining geological ages.

Protactinium, the Mother Substance of Actinium—Work with Lise Meitner

Now let me return to my own early work at Dahlem. The main areas of investigation that occupied Lise Meitner and me were the various still incompletely known radioactive elements, their emission of beta and gamma rays, and the systematic photographing of the magnetic beta-ray pictures of the various elements. Of special interest were two substances recently discovered by others, which were labeled uranium-Y and uranium-X_2.

In connection with uranium-Y, there was a controversy about whether it existed at all. We were able to establish its existence as well as its half-life and to show that it had the same chemical characteristics as thorium and, like thorium, originated by the ejection of an alpha particle from the nucleus of a uranium atom.

As for uranium-X_2, we were able to confirm the opinion of the discoverers, Kasimir Fajans and O. Göhring, that it was a product of uranium-X_1. At that time a new theory, which was called the "radioactive transfer," was first being discussed by various researchers—its final triumph was Soddy's recognition of isotopes. According to this theory, uranium-X_2 must fill a hitherto empty space in the system of chemical elements, because its beta-ray transmission had to result in an atom with five valences—that is, a homologue of tantalum, or eka-tantalum. Fajans and Göhring were therefore justified in naming a new substance. They chose the name "brevium," which was quite good, because the half-life of this substance was only a little more than 1 minute—we found a median value of 1.17 minutes; the currently accepted value is 1.14 minutes.

The discovery of uranium-X_2, or brevium, as will be seen, made it important to discover the mother substance of actinium. But this was an especially difficult problem.

The radioactive element actinium is a constant companion of uranium in all minerals which contain uranium; the percentage of actinium is proportionate to the amount of uranium in the mineral. Actinium does not have a long half-life. Madame Curie had guessed it at about 30 years, but the real value is considerably lower—13.5 years. Therefore actinium must be formed by uranium or one of the uranium decay products. Assuming that no intermediate substance was formed, this fact should have been easy to prove, but this was not the case. Therefore a long-lived substance had to exist between uranium and actinium.

A great diversity of possibilities was considered. Soddy was actually on the right track; he formed the hypothesis that the mother substance might be a decay product of the beta-ray-emitting uranium-X (four valences) and eka-tantalum, and that this element, which had to have five valences, by emitting alpha particles, changed into actinium with three valences. At the same time eka-tantalum was thought to produce, via beta-ray emission, uranium-II, with six valences, the starting point of the ionium-radium series. But the discovery of the short-lived uranium-X_2 (brevium), showed that Soddy's scheme must be wrong somewhere—there was now no space for a long-lived eka-tantalum.

The team of Hahn and Meitner therefore proposed a scheme which assumed that uranium-X can decay in two different ways, either into the short-lived brevium, or into a still unknown long-lived mother substance of actinium, with the same chemical characteristics as brevium. Now the problem was to find a substance with the chemical characteristics of brevium—a higher homologue of tantalum. A similar idea had been expressed by Göhring, one of the discoverers of brevium, but he concluded his discussion with the words: "Some experiments with the purpose of discovering a new member of the brevium-pleiades were carried out, looking for a possible mother substance of actinium. But the existence of such a substance could not be proved, either with pitchblende or with ionium or uranium-X." We did not let this judgment discourage us, however, especially after we had satisfied ourselves that radium was *not* the mother substance of actinium.

But then an event occurred that was to create a long interruption in the work started at the Kaiser Wilhelm Institute for Chemistry; in August 1914 World War One began. I was immediately drafted as a vice-sergeant in the *Landwehr* [reserves]. Lise Meitner stayed at the Institute, but not for long. She volunteered for service in the Austrian army and served behind the front lines as an X-ray technician.

Early in 1915 I became a lieutenant in the *Landwehr* and Professor Fritz Haber saw to it that I was transferred to a group of "active specialists." In 1917 I was transferred to Supreme Hearquarters, and in this capacity had official contact with the military research carried out in Haber's Institute in Dahlem. This provided an opportunity to look in at the nearby Kaiser Wilhelm Institute and to think about science a little. Lise Meitner had also returned from her war service and we tentatively resumed our work, returning to our search for the mother substance of actinium, the unknown homologue of tantalum.

Our first search was for suitable raw material. We inspected the leftover material that results from the treatment of pitchblende with nitric acid. The substance remaining consists mainly of silicon dioxide, which does not dissolve in nitric acid. Careful work revealed that it contained very small quantities of radium, radiolead, and ionium, but also virtually all the tantalum-like substances of the pitchblende. Therefore the substance we were looking for could be expected to be somewhat more enriched than radium in the same preparation. This suspicion was somewhat strengthened by the observation that the pitchblende residue produced considerably earlier gave off some actinium emanation in addition to weak thorium emanation.

The suspicion that pitchblende residue was a useful raw material turned out to be correct. We succeeded in finding the unknown element and in proving it to be the mother substance of actinium. We proposed the name of proto-actinium (later contracted to protactinium).

Our very comprehensive report, submitted in March 1918, contained the following summary of the results of our work:

1. The previously hypothetical mother substance of actinium has been found and prepared in alkali acids in radioactively pure form. It is a homologue of tantalum.
2. It emits alpha rays with a penetration of 3.14 centimeters.
3. The half-life is a minimum of 1200 years and a maximum of 180,000 years.

4. The formation of actinium was proved by:
   a. The alpha ray curves that were established
   b. The measurements of actinium emanation, the steady increase of which could be observed daily for a period of several months
   c. The active deposit which we could find in increasing amounts on negatively charged plates.
5. Furthermore, Madame Curie's value for the half-life of actinium has been verified.
6. The name proto-actinium [later protactinium] has been chosen for the new element.

The position of the new substance in the uranium series had to be reformulated, because the scheme we had proposed in 1913 could not be maintained. Since uranium-X_2 (brevium) is certainly the offspring of uranium-X_1, we assumed uranium-Y (meanwhile recognized as an isotope of uranium-X) to be the mother substance of protactinium. This is indeed the case, but our scheme was still wrong, because the third isotope of uranium, actino-uranium (now called uranium-235) which is the mother substance of uranium-Y, was not then known. Its existence was established spectroscopically at a later date. We therefore thought that the known uranium-II, the mother substance of ionium, was also the mother substance of uranium-Y, both of which had four valences. Under the circumstances this was a pardonable mistake.

Because of the war, we did not know about a publication by Soddy and J. A. Cranston, which appeared at about the same time as our own report and also dealt with the mother substance of actinium. Soddy and Cranston tried to obtain this substance from pitchblende by a method of sublimation. The preparations obtained emitted increasing amounts of actinium emanation, revealing an increasing concentration of actinium. Using certain assumptions, Soddy and Cranston calculated a half-life for actinium of roughly 3500 years. In reality the half-life is less than 1 percent of this figure, which proves that these researchers could have had only traces of the new element in their preparations. They could not obtain any information about the characteristics of the new substance. Later Soddy and Cranston agreed to our name (protactinium) for the element which had been tentatively designated as eka-tantalum.

But the name for element no. 91, between thorium and uranium, does not completely comply with usage. Fajans and Göhring, the original discoverers of that element, had had the right to name it; they had called it brevium, because of its short half-life. But the International Atomic Commission could not bring itself to use the name brevium for the element we had discovered, since it had a half-life of many thousands of years. A fully correct designation would be "protactinium (Pa), the long-lived isotope of brevium."

After the war protactinium became the subject of a great many investigations, of which only a few can be mentioned. One dealt with the separation of protactinium from pitchblende; one with the origin of actinium, in which an effort was made to determine where the actinium series and the uranium series diverge; one with protactinium and the half-life of actinium, for which the values of 20 years ± 10 percent was found; and one with the half-life of protactinium (12,000 years was found to be the lower limit) and the percentage of it in uranium minerals. All these investigations were carried out by the team of Hahn and Meitner.

Of course we discussed the possibility of obtaining quantities of the long-lived element sufficient to register on a sensitive scale and looked for a method of a powerful enrichment of the raw material. In a small way we succeeded in separating the new substance out of the raw material along with its lower homologue tantalum and then found ways to separate it from the tantalum. But we were not very successful.

However, my co-worker Aristide von Grosse concluded from a detailed comparison of the characteristics of both thorium and uranium with those of their lower homologues that they showed rather pronounced differences and might resemble the elements of other vertical groupings. For this reason he expected a certain similarity between protactinium and zirconium and tried an enrichment of protactinium by using zirconium compounds. His success was extraordinary. He precipitated protactinium with zirconium phosphate from an acid solution, thereby separating it from the tantalum that was present. He succeeded in obtaining 2 milligrams of protactinium pentoxide, 270,000 times as active as the same amount of uranium, from half a kilogram of material which we had slightly enriched and had estimated contained about 4 milligrams of protactinium pentoxide. The chemical characteristics of protactinium, which von Grosse had predicted, were so pronounced that the separation of protactinium and zirconium from the material, and even the later concentration of the protactinium and the zirconium, was not at all difficult. Walling, using independent methods, also determined the half-life of protactinium to be 20,000 years. After we had established the existence of actino-uranium by means of the mass spectroscope and found the percentage of actino-uranium, the mother substance of protactinium, our figure for the half-life was 32,000 years.

At a later date my colleagues G. Graue and H. Käding succeeded in extracting 700 milligrams of protactinium from 5.5 tons of uranium minerals from Joachimsthal, from which the radium had already been removed. These 5.5 tons contained an estimated 950 milligrams of protactinium in all. Of the 700 milligrams extracted, 500 milligrams of the protactinium were in the form of beautifully crystallized protactinium-potassium-fluoride; the remainder was in less rich form. The chemical similarity of protactinium and tantalum was utilized in this work. The working of the 5.5 tons of raw material was done at the Deutsche Gasglühlicht Auer Company in Oranienburg, with financial aid from the Notgemeinschaft der deutschen Wissenschaft [Emergency Association of German Science]; the final concentration at the Kaiser Wilhelm Institute for Chemistry.

Protactinium thus became the second naturally radioactive element to be made available in a quantity sufficient for use in chemical experimentation and research—radium had of course been the first.

Uranium-Z, First Example of a Nuclear Isomer

Some years ago the physicist A. Flammersfeld devoted some space to the question of whether the discoveries made by researchers are the ones they were pursuing or whether the discovery that finally rewards them for their hard work is entirely different from what they had intended to find.[2] He concluded that about half the experimental discoveries of the twentieth century contradicted the discoverer's original idea and therefore must be classed as experiments with a surprise result, citing as examples the main discoveries in the field of radioactivity, the discovery of atomic number, and the dis-

[2] *Author's Note.* In his article "Zur Geschichte der Kernisomerie" [History of Nuclear Isomers], in *Beiträge zur Physik und Chemie des 20. Jahrhunderts* [Contributions to Physics and Chemistry in the Twentieth Century], Braunschweig: Friedr. Vieweg and Son, 1959.

covery of isotopes, each of which in turn changed the definition of the concept "atom" until finally it was realized that the nature of an atom can be defined by the mass of its nucleus and the number of units of charge in the nucleus. He concluded by saying: "This concept remained valid until the middle thirties, even though one exception had been known since 1921. Nobody knew what to do with this exception, which had been discovered by Otto Hahn. The history of its discovery is particularly interesting because Hahn was looking for something else."

Indeed, I often discovered one thing while I was looking for something different, as my examples in the preceding chapters have shown. What I named "radioactive recoil" was recognized as a special phenomenon only after I had been compelled to drop a suspected new product in the series of elements formed by the decay of actinium—mainly because a radioactive substance that had been proved to be quite inactive chemically was found in places where, because of its relative chemical inertness, it simply could not be. The "emanation method" (see page 126) was developed after a search for a suspected radium-X as the source of beta rays that seemed to come from alpha-radiating radium had proved futile.

A rather similar situation led to the finding of the first example of a nuclear isomer among radioactive atoms. From that find a more precise description of the characteristics of radioactive nuclei could be derived.

After the discovery of protactinium concluded the long search for the mother substance of actinium, its position relative to uranium was still unknown. We suspected a branching of uranium decay, with the recently discovered uranium-Y as a result. Uranium-Y was possibly the mother substance of protactinium. The process was supposed to take place parallel to the main decay series of uranium into uranium-X_1 and uranium-X_2 which led to uranium-II, the mother substance of ionium and the beginning of the radium series. Actino-uranium, the actual mother substance of protactinium and actinium (which has nothing to do with uranium-I and uranium-II) was found much later by means of the mass-spectroscope.

Professor K. Hermann in Charlottenburg suspected the existence of a heavy uranium of a mass of about 240, in order to explain the atomic weight of ordinary uranium (then determined as 238.2), which was too high in relationship to the atomic weight of radium (226).[3] Finally there were attempts at explanation by utilizing the recently discovered helium isotope of mass 3 instead of the normal alpha particle of mass 4.

In spite of the discovery of protactinium and uranium-Y, the actinium series was by no means clear, especially since the joint work which Lise Meitner and I did on uranium-X and protactinium occasionally revealed small discrepancies in the electroscope readings. When discrepancies occurred more than once, they had to be investigated and explained, especially because of the possibility that there might be another unknown series of uranium decay with a lesser intensity.

If such a series existed, it should have been possible to find one or another of its members. Since additional uranium isotopes could not be discovered chemically, I checked once more on the radioactive performance of the first decay products, uranium-Y with a half-life of 25 hours and uranium-X with a half-life of 24 days, as well as on that of protactinium. But the enriched uranium-Y preparations did not show any indications from which the existence of a new product could be suspected. Protactinium, or uranium-X $(X_1 + X_2)$, however, was different. Protactinium that had been separated from the

[3] *Author's Note.* To the best of my knowledge he never published his idea.

uranium solution with the aid of tantalic acid showed—if you worked fast—some radioactivity of unknown origin; this diminished faster than that from uranium-X_1, and more slowly than that from uranium-X_2. The beta activity was only one-tenth of 1 percent of the beta activity of the uranium salts. The half-life of more than 6 but less than 7 hours suggested the actinium isotope mesothorium-2 with its half-life of 6.2 hours. This possibility was the more credible since powerful mesothorium preparations were present in our Institute.

Using brand-new glass and platinum vessels, I was able to show that the unknown substance was not mesothorium-2 and that there had been no contamination with known substances, though the low level of activity suggested that possibility.

The substance was finally recognized as an isotope of protactinium; it was separated from uranium-X_1. Since there was already a uranium-Y, it was named uranium-Z. We succeeded in obtaining preparations that were 99.5 percent pure as far as radioactivity went. Because of the percentage rate at which this substance was formed by uranium-X, this purity proved that the separation of the new substance from uranium-X had been successful for one part in one hundred-thousandth. The results of this work were summarized as follows:

1. Ordinary uranium salts contain a new radioactive substance with the chemical characteristics of protactinium.
2. It emits beta rays and has a half-life of 6.7 hours.
3. The rays are of great complexity; halving their intensity requires (within the limits of the investigation) from 0.014 to 0.12 millimeters of aluminum.
4. The radiation intensity of the new substance is equal to 2.5 per thousand of that of uranium-X ($X_1 + X_2$) from the same quantity of uranium.
5. The mother substance must be either uranium-X_1 or else a new uranium-X_1 isotope of similar half-life. If the former

98

is the case, uranium-X_1 must disintegrate in two different ways, something that has not yet been observed with radioactive substances. If the latter is correct, then the most probable suggestion is the assumption of a new uranium decay chain with low radiation intensity, the members of which insert themselves into the well-known uranium-radium chain.

Until the problem of the mother substance has been cleared up, the new substance shall be known as uranium-Z.

Though I had stated two possibilities, I did not think that uranium-X_1, with its half-life of 24 days, could be the mother substance; two different kinds of decay, both under beta-ray emission, would have been an entirely new process.

As had happened to me before—for example, when I did *not* proclaim the existence of isotopes in spite of overwhelming proof of the chemical identity of numerous radioactive elements—I was extremely reluctant to announce as a new discovery a result that did not conform to existing ideas. I therefore concentrated on finding a new low-intensity chain of uranium decay. Since uranium-Z had been associated with uranium-X $(X_1 + X_2)$, the unknown mother substance of uranium-Z had to be somewhere in the uranium-X. Now, if uranium-X *contained* the unknown mother substance, the ratio of uranium-X to uranium-Z would change with time. But if uranium-X *were* the mother substance, the ratio would remain constant. The progression of the work was to determine as precisely as possible the amount of uranium-Z in uranium-X preparations of different ages.

While a test for the presence of uranium-Z in powerful uranium-X preparations was quite simple, determinations of quantities over extended periods of time were difficult and at first unreliable. After all, I was dealing with preparations which, when they were measured and their radioactive purity ascertained at the same time, never had more than one-tenth of 1 percent of the beta activity of uranium-X. To make it worse, the carrier for the uranium-Z was tantalum, which cannot be checked by a simple chemical reaction. To avoid any possibility of contamination, all the laboratory equipment for this work was new, and the work was carried out in a room reserved for this purpose. The comparison that had to be made was between lanthanum oxide + uranium-X on the one side and tantalum oxide + uranium-Z on the other; but it was hard to obtain reliable values, even when the uranium-X was of known and equal age, because the dispersion of the radiation from the uranium-Z was too great.

Finally I shifted to an indicator method, using protactinium as an indicator for the amounts of uranium-Z. Instead of pure tantalic acid as carrier for the uranium-Z, I used a carefully checked tantalic-acid protactinium preparation. The amount of uranium-Z could then be determined by the constant activity of the protactinium that had been recovered by separation. I developed a method for reliable measurements of the alpha-radiating indicator protactinium. This was a somewhat tedious but reliable method and a number of determinations of uranium-Z could be made. The uranium-Z had of course been derived from uranium-X, and the latter had been separated from a quantity of uranium that weighed several kilograms. The ratio of uranium-X to uranium-Z remained constant, which argued against my original opinion that there was an unknown mother substance for the uranium-Z.

But since I still could not bring myself to make an announcement about two chains of decay, I made a large-scale experiment. The purpose was to have so much uranium-X that, even after it had decayed to 1 percent of its starting intensity, the presence of uranium-Z, with an intensity of only one-thousandth of the total, could still be determined.

With some aid from the chemical factory of Kahlbaum in Berlin we extracted the uranium-X from 100 kilograms of uranium nitrate. Then I had a very powerful quantity of uranium-X, free of all impurities, and could use the indicator method for checking on uranium-Z as the uranium-X decayed; the last determination was made after 156 days, when the intensity of the uranium-X had fallen to about 1 percent of its original value. The results can be seen in the following table:

Table 2 The yield of uranium-Z from uranium-X preparations of different ages

Age of uranium-X (in days)	Amount of uranium-X still existing at the time (percent)	Activity of uranium-Z (measured through 0.07 millimeters of aluminum) in thousandths of activity of uranium-X
2	94.0	1.14
4	88.8	1.17
5	86.5	1.07
12	70.6	1.19
15	64.8	1.14
18	59.4	1.15
53	21.7	1.27
82	9.4	1.14
97	6.0	1.34
136	1.95	1.18
156	1.07	—
		mean: 1.18

Disregarding the failure of the last of these experiments, the ratio can be seen to be virtually the same; considering the complications of the method used, it is a surprisingly good result. An unknown mother substance of uranium-Z would have to have the same half-life (24 days) as the known uranium-X. This was so improbable that I concluded that uranium-Z was not derived from an unknown substance, but that under emission of beta rays, uranium-X is changed into the short-lived uranium-X_2, and that, at the same time, a very small percentage of it turns into uranium-Z, which is also a beta-ray emitter.

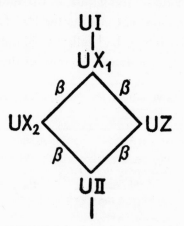

Figure 2. Simultaneous production of uranium-Z and uranium-X₂ from uranium-X₁

If we recall that the starting point of the whole investigation had been the then inexplicable discrepancy between the atomic weights of uranium and of radium, leading to the assumption of an unknown chain of uranium decay, we must admit that I found something quite different from what I had been looking for. Uranium-Z represented the first case of a nuclear isomer. But this discovery had hardly any influence on later research into isomers. As Flammersfeld said, the discovery happened about fifteen years too soon, which is unusual in modern research. Admittedly the case of uranium-Z was quite complicated and the answer was hard to find. But there is a kind of rule—well known to physicists familiar with the history of their own science—that it is in very complicated matters that discoveries are normally made; the simple cases do not show up until later. Further progress in the discovery of nuclear isomers had to wait until the discovery of artificially induced radioactivity had provided researchers with many more types of nuclei. By now about 160 pairs of nuclear isomers are known and most of them have been well investigated.

Work with Lise Meitner on Beta and Gamma Rays

The experiments involving beta rays carried out in collaboration with Lise Meitner at the Chemical Institute of the University of Berlin had been begun under the working hypothesis that specific radioactive elements will send out beta rays of a specific energy and that their absorption in aluminum takes place under an exponential law. The photographing of "magnetic spectra" with Otto von Baeyer had caused the first doubts. The sharp beta-ray lines from mesothorium-2, for example, and the washed-out bands of penetrating rays had proved that our simple assumptions could not be correct. But we did find several new beta-emitting substances and developed methods for distinguishing the different beta-emitting radio elements. We had also worked out methods for obtaining the different substances in thin layers.

After World War One was over, I continued this work at the Kaiser Wilhelm Institute for Chemistry, again in collaboration with Lise Meitner. An investigation of gamma rays from thorium products showed that the alpha-radiating thorium—aside from the active deposit thorium-B and thorium-C—emitted characteristic soft gamma rays. Radioactinium, another alpha-ray emitter, also sent out gamma rays. In the gamma rays from uranium-$X_1 + X_2$ we succeeded in distinguishing three groups, and with the aid of a fast-acting method of chemical separation we could assign these gamma-ray groups to the substance (uranium-X_1 or X_2) from which they originated.

We also had a method for distinguishing various sealed preparations of radium and of mesothorium with the aid of the gamma rays they emitted. Mesothorium preparations were then used in comparatively large quantities both in medicine and in industry as a substitute for radium. It was desirable to be able to distinguish between fresh mesothorium and radium, fresh mesothorium and old mesothorium (that is, mesothorium which was free of radiothorium, and that which was not), and old mesothorium and radium. Our very thorough report showed that it was easy to tell radium from fresh mesothorium and fresh mesothorium from old, but also that it was possible to distinguish old mesothorium from radium.

The weight of the work on beta and gamma rays shifted more and more in the direction of Lise Meitner's Physical-Radioactive Department with its growing staff of researchers. Chemistry provided assistance in the form of improved methods for making the preparations and by speeding up the production where necessary. Since there were many cases where many cases where a substance was composed of several beta-ray emitters—radiothorium or radioactinium or radium, each with its decay products—and we had to determine which beta-ray group originated from which element, ways had to be found to separate the mother substance quickly and with high purity. Only then could one tell which rays came from the mother substance and which from the decay products. For photographing the beta spectra a method that had originated with J. Danysz (Figure 3) was adopted; it produced a better separation of the lines. With the aid of this device two beta-ray groups which had originally been ascribed to thorium-X were found to come from radiothorium.

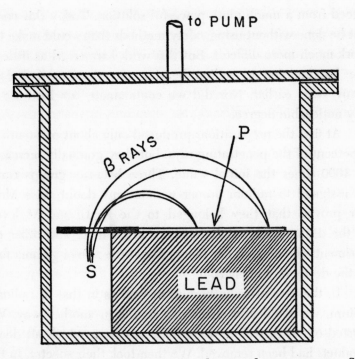

Figure 3. Danysz's instrument for obtaining beta-ray spectra. S = source of radiation; P = photographic plate

An electrolytic method for producing a thin layer of radium which was fairly free of decay products was especially interesting. A solution of radium chloride was first heated in a water bath for several hours; this removed emanation and the active deposit. Then carbon dioxide was blown in gently and the resulting radium carbonate was deposited on a thin platinum wire. The thin layer, which had a white color, was brought to gentle red heat in order to make the salt nonemanating. The strength of the resulting preparation varied between 0.3 and 1 milligram of radium.

Nowadays, during the 1960s, it is interesting to remember how much more freely we worked with radium 35 or 40 years ago, for the wires with 0.3 to 1 milligram of radium were produced from a much more powerful solution. Today this could not be done without using safety methods that would make the work much more difficult. But this work harmed us as little as the fractionation of radium-bearing mesothorium had done many years earlier. Nor did we contaminate our Institute to any noticeable degree.

At first the preparations produced only about one-tenth of 1 percent of the penetrating rays, but they gradually increased to 1000 times the initial value. Three beta-ray groups could be assigned to radium proper without any doubt; Lise Meitner proved that they belonged to the K, L, and M levels of the disintegrating radium atom. From these and other experiments she derived her theory about the role of gamma rays in the decay of a nucleus.

In the case of radiothorium as well as in that of radioactinium, we could also check our results in another way. We started out with well-purified materials from which all decay products had been removed. We then took their spectra, in the case of actinium that of actinium-X, with the active deposit and that of the active deposit alone, for thorium that of originally pure thorium-X and that of the gradually forming active deposit. Our improved equipment produced spectra with many lines, and each of them could be assigned to the type of atom that had produced it.

Radioactinium and its decay products may be cited as an example of how complicated these spectra grew with the systematic improvement of equipment and procedure. Radioactinium produced forty-nine beta-ray groups and actinium-X produced twenty-one groups. Lise Meitner assigned these groups to various isotopes and then tried to determine whether the transformation of gamma rays from the nucleus of the atom into beta rays (that is, secondary electrons) takes place in the electron shells of the original atom or in those of the newly formed atom. She was able to show that the electrons come from the newly formed atom and that gamma rays are therefore emitted *after* the disintegration of the original atom. These results settled an argument with C. D. Ellis and H. W. B. Skinner that had been going on for years.

Lise Meitner and Orthmann then tried to investigate the primary beta rays from the nucleus which could not be understood. She gave much thought to possible explanations before Wolfgang Pauli solved this puzzle by postulating the mysterious neutrino.

The voluminous work on beta and gamma rays which Lise Meitner carried out at the Kaiser Wilhelm Institute for Chemistry does not belong in this book, since it was all done by her and her co-workers without any contribution on my part.

The Year 1933 and Fritz Haber

The year 1933 was marked by an interruption of my experimental research, by a closer personal cooperation with our neighboring institute, the Kaiser Wilhelm Institute for Physical Chemistry and Electrochemistry, and last but not least by a close relationship with the director of that Institute, Privy Councilor Fritz Haber.

For the early part of 1933 I had accepted an invitation to be a visiting lecturer at the George Fisher Baker Institute for Chemistry of Cornell University in Ithaca, New York. This lectureship was expected to continue about four months. Hitler's "Seizure of Power" occurred on January 30, 1933, but I did not believe that his regime would last long. Without any serious concern for the future, I left Dahlem for the United States at the end of February 1933.

But the reports I received in confidential letters from Berlin about the treatment of Jewish professors worried me greatly. The situation grew worse month by month, especially at Professor Haber's Institute. Haber himself was not molested at first, but some of his very capable Jewish co-workers were discharged. People who were members of the Nazi Party or of one of its organizations were dictating policy at the Institute. Finally Haber decided to surrender his post as director. In a letter addressed to the newly appointed Minister of Education [*Kultusminister*] he stated that he did not wish to be treated differently from his Jewish co-workers.

My lectures in Ithaca were finished in June, and I started out on a trip to other American universities, which had been planned to extend all the way to California. But the news from Dahlem was so ominous that I decided, largely on the advice of friends who were concerned about Haber's Institute, to cancel my trip to the West Coast and return to Germany as quickly as possible.[4]

When I got back to Berlin, the president of the Kaiser Wilhelm Institute, Privy Councilor Max Planck, as well as Professor Haber, asked me to serve for a time as acting director of Haber's Institute, in addition to being director of my own Institute. Haber, who had been in ill health for years, accepted an invitation from Cambridge University and went to England. As acting director I tried to soften especially harsh orders from the people in power, but of course I could not do anything about the general situation. After a few weeks I was informed that a new director had been appointed for all Insti-

[4] *Author's Note.* Many years later a generous grant from the Ford Foundation enabled me to make the trip which was canceled in 1933. The invitation and the grant originated with E. O. Lawrence of the Radiation Laboratory of the University of California in Berkeley, after he learned of the circumstances behind my return to Germany.

tutes and that my activity as acting director was therefore at an end. But there was no change in my own Institute for Chemistry.

Fritz Haber, a broken man, died on January 29, 1934, during a vacation in Switzerland. His death was not mentioned in the German press; only Max von Laue had the courage to write an obituary in *Die Naturwissenschaften* which almost got him into serious trouble. Professor Max Bodenstein mentioned Haber's death at a meeting of the Prussian Academy of Science.

During the year 1934 requests came from several quarters for a memorial meeting for Fritz Haber, to be held on the anniversary of his death. Privy Councilor Planck personally supervised the planning. Three main speeches were planned, to follow short introductory remarks: one about Haber's importance during World War One by Dr. Joseph Koeth, a retired Colonel; one about his importance as a scientist by Professor Karl-Friedrich Bonhoeffer of Leipzig; and one about his personality and his services to the Kaiser Wilhelm Institute, which I prepared.

At first the outlook seemed quiet enough and the invitations, containing the program, were mailed about the tenth of January. But on the fifteenth the Minister of Education for Prussia sent a message to the Dean of the Engineering College [*Technische Hochschule*], in which the planned meeting was described as "a provocation of the National-Socialist State." The final sentences of the message read: "This interpretation is strengthened by the fact that the originators of the invitation had the audacity to suggest the wearing of uniforms by the guests. I therefore feel compelled to forbid attendance at the memorial meeting by all officials and employees under my jurisdiction."

A letter to the Minister by Privy Councilor Planck was answered politely enough, with an explanation of the reasons

Die Kaiser-Wilhelm-Gesellschaft
zur Förderung der Wissenschaften
beehrt sich
in Gemeinschaft mit der
Deutschen Chemischen Gesellschaft
und der Deutschen Physikalischen Gesellschaft
zu einer
Gedächtnisfeier für
Fritz Haber
am Dienstag, den 29. Januar 1935, 12 Uhr mittags,
im Harnack-Haus, Berlin-Dahlem, Ihnestraße 16—20,
einzuladen.

1. Andante con moto (Thema mit Variationen)
   aus dem Quartett Nr. 14 von Franz Schubert

2. Einleitende Worte
   Geheimrat Prof. Dr. Max Planck, Präsident der Kaiser-Wilhelm-Gesellschaft zur Förderung der Wissenschaften

3. Gedächtnisreden
   Prof. Dr. Otto Hahn, Direktor des Kaiser-Wilhelm-Instituts für Chemie
   Oberst a. D. Dr.-Ing. e. h. Joseph Koeth
   Prof. Dr. Karl-Friedrich Bonhoeffer, Auswärtiges wissenschaftliches Mit-
   glied des Kaiser-Wilhelm-Instituts für physikalische Chemie und Elektro-
   chemie

4. Cavatine (adagio molto espressivo)
   aus dem Quartett op. 130 von Ludwig van Beethoven
   Die Mitglieder des Philharmonischen Orchesters:
   Konzertmeister Siegfried Borries (1. Violine), Karl Höver (2. Violine),
   Reinhard Wolf (Viola), Wolfram Kleber (Cello).

Uniform oder dunkler Anzug

Figure 4. Invitation for the memorial ceremony for Fritz Haber

Translation of the invitation on facing page:

The Kaiser Wilhelm Society
for the Promulgation of the Sciences,
in cooperation with the
German Chemical Society
and the German Physical Society,
requests the honor of your presence at a
Memorial Meeting for Fritz Haber
on Thursday, January 29, 1935, at 12 noon
at Harnack House, Berlin-Dahlem, Ihne Street No. 16–20

1. *Andante con moto* (Theme and Variations) from the Quartet No. 14 by Franz Schubert
2. Introductory Remarks, Professor Dr. Max Planck, President of the Kaiser Wilhelm Society.
3. Lecturers in memoriam: Professor Dr. Otto Hahn, Director of the Kaiser Wilhelm Institute for Chemistry
   Colonel (retired) Dr.-Eng. Joseph Koeth
   Professor Dr. Karl-Friedrich Bonhoeffer, member of the Kaiser Wilhelm Institute for Physical Chemistry and Electrochemistry
4. Cavatina (*Adagio molto expressivo*) from the Quartet, opus 130, by Ludwig van Beethoven
   Concertmaster Siegfried Borris (first violin), Karl Höver (second violin), Reinhard Wolf (viola), Wolfram Kleber (cello).

Uniform or dark suit.

---

for the edict. But then a more sharply worded message arrived. The "Deputy of the Führer" accused the societies involved of lack of tact and stated that no member of any of the societies of the RTA [5] would attend. In my own Institute a declaration by the Society of German Chemists was posted.

[5] *Translator's Note. Reichsgemeinschaft der Technisch-Wissenschaftlichen Arbeit*—The Realm's Union of Technological-Scientific Work.

In spite of this initial prohibition, the meeting was not canceled.

This was the grotesque situation which existed when Planck called for me at my Institute in the forenoon of January 29, 1935. We weren't sure that we would not be prevented by physical force from entering Harnack House, where the meeting was being held. But nothing happened.

The beautiful big hall was crowded. Among those present were several of Haber's relatives, but—more important—Privy Councilor Bosch of I. G. Farbenindustrie and many high executives of the company whom Bosch had invited by telegram were also there. Wives of many of the professors who were not permitted to attend were present, as were several personal friends of Haber. On the back benches there were some members of my Institute: Lise Meitner, Fritz Strassmann, and Max Delbrück.

The meeting was dignified and impressive. Professor Bonhoeffer could not deliver his own speech—he would have been discharged from his post at the University of Leipzig if he had done so—but at his request I read it for him. I had resigned from the faculty of the University of Berlin in 1934 and was therefore in less danger.

The only further development was still another order from the Ministry of Education: it was forbidden to publish any reports on the meeting and the speeches made were not to be published either.

The whole episode shows that during the early years of the Hitler regime some resistance—minor, to be sure—was still possible; at a somewhat later date no such possibility remained.

Verein deutscher Chemiker e. V., Berlin W 35, Potsdamer Str. 103a

Gemäß Verfügung des Präsidenten der RTA., Herrn Dr. Ing. Todt ist die Teilnahme an der Gedächtnisfeier für Fritz Haber am 29. Januar 1935 im Harnackhaus allen Mitgliedern des Vereins deutscher Chemiker e. V. untersagt.

Berlin, den 25. Januar 1935

Verein Deutscher Chemiker e. V.

Figure 5. Order of the Society of German Chemists forbidding its members to attend the Haber memorial ceremony

Translation of the declaration above:

Society of German Chemists, Berlin W. 35, Potsdamer Street, 103A.

In accordance with the order of the President of the RTA, Doctor of Engineering Todt, members of the Society of German Chemists are not permitted to attend the Memorial Meeting for Fritz Haber on January 29, 1935 at Harnack House.

Berlin, January 25, 1935 Society of German Chemists.

Some Examples of
Applied Radiochemistry

Precipitation and adsorption of small amounts of matter; normal and anomalistic mixed crystals

After the discovery of protactinium, the long-lived mother substance of actinium, and the finding of the protactinium isotope uranium-Z as the first example of nuclear isomers, it looked for a while as if all naturally occurring radioactive elements were known. At a later date I looked again for long-lived isotopes of radium and actinium but failed to find them. During the years following the study of protactinium and of uranium-Z I carried out the studies on beta and gamma rays with Lise Meitner which have been mentioned, but I also devoted much time to the study of applied radiochemistry. These studies were carried out with a whole staff of collaborators.

Since an account of this work was published in 1936 by the Cornell University Press as a book entitled *Applied Radiochemistry*, it is not necessary to include the details here, but I want to give a quick survey of the work done. Following an introduction dealing with the theoretical and experimental foundations of radiochemistry, the book contained three main chapters with the following headings:

I. Investigations on Radioactive Atoms in Quantities Too Small to Be Weighed
II. Indicator Methods
III. The Emanation Method.

The investigations of nonweighable quantities of radioactive elements had been begun by Fajans and Paneth. At first it was impossible to predict how such substances would behave in the presence of other substances in quantities that could be weighed. They might be precipitated along with another precipitate; they might be adsorbed by such a precipitate; they might stay in solution; or they might do something else that was unforeseeable. These various possibilities were of great importance to the radiochemist. The researches carried out during 1913 and 1914 by Fajans and Paneth were summarized as "Fajans's Precipitation Rule" and "Paneth's Adsorption Rule." The Precipitation Rule read: "A radioactive element will be precipitated from a very dilute solution along with the precipitate of a stable element if the conditions are such that the radioactive element would be precipitated by itself if it were present in weighable quantities."

This rule provided a guide for checking on the chemical nature of the radioactive elements; in fact, the chemical characteristics of these greatly diluted substances could be obtained with remarkable precision. K. Horovitz and Paneth then asked themselves whether a special kind of adsorption, strongly influenced by the chemical nature of the substances, could be held responsible for their astonishingly definite behavior. Paneth conducted a series of adsorption experiments with salts and oxides of poor solubility and formulated his rule: A substance will adsorb such radioactive elements as have analogous compounds poorly soluble in the solvent in question. Here the term "analogous compound" means a compound of the radioactive element with the electrically negative parts of the adsorbing substance. But since these substances are usually typical ion lattices, Paneth's rule could also be formulated as follows:

"An ion lattice will adsorb those ions which are poorly soluble in the solvent in question if they form compounds with those parts of the ion lattice that carry the opposite electrical charge."

The two rules by Fajans and Paneth worked well and a large number of observations could be explained from this point of view. But in the course of time I began to notice that there were also quite a number of exceptions. I therefore instigated a systematic study of the problems of precipitation and adsorption. To take care of—actually to eliminate—the exceptions, I formulated the following two rules:

Hahn's Precipitation Rule: "An element that is present in a state of high dilution will be precipitated along with a crystallizing precipitate if it can fit into the crystal lattice of the precipitate—that is to say, if it can form mixed crystals with the ions of the crystallizing precipitate. If it cannot do this, it will remain in solution, even if its compounds with the portion of the lattice carrying the opposite charge are difficult to dissolve in the solvent in question."

Hahn's Adsorption Rule: "An element that is present in a state of high dilution will be adsorbed by a precipitate if the precipitate has been made to carry a surface charge opposite to that of the element to be adsorbed, provided that the element to be adsorbed is only poorly soluble in the solvent in question.

These two rules caused a lively discussion, chiefly between Fajans and his collaborators on one side and myself and my collaborators on the other. Both sides cited experiments that were favorable (or seemed to be favorable) to their own formulations. The opposing viewpoints were reconciled in time, but my statement about the forming of mixed crystals when two substances were precipitated together proved to be very useful and led to additional consequences that will be mentioned later. My adsorption rule had to be limited slightly in some respects. Later I carried out a series of experiments with L. Imre which dealt specifically with problems of adsorption. These led to a distinction between ion adsorption and colloid adsorption, and also to an addition to the adsorption rule with reference to easily soluble compounds and to a distinction between strongly polarized and weakly polarized lattices.

Imre continued this work independently in Budapest, his native city, extending it to investigations of adsorption on coagulating precipitates and to the kinetics of crystal lattices. He began to distinguish between boundary layer balances and inner balances in heterogeneous systems. I had no hand in his later work and I also lacked the mathematical foundations for the more theoretical assumptions and calculations. But my intensive interest in adsorption had taught me to pay attention to such phenomena and to avoid erroneous conclusions.

The conclusions from complicated experiments were easier to formulate with my precipitation rule, which states that during joint precipitation of a radioactive element present in trace amounts only and of a relatively abundant element, the "micro-component" forms mixed crystals with the "macro-component." But these mixed crystals are formed in different ways, depending on circumstances. There are homogeneous mixed crystals— that is, crystals in which the micro-component is evenly distributed in the macro-component. But there are also crystals in which the micro-component is present in the interior of the crystal in disproportionate amounts; depending on its solubility it may be greatly enriched or else the opposite is the case. In the former case the distribution is governed by "Nernst's rule"; in the latter a logarithmic law applies.

The classical method of making pure radium salts via fractional crystallization of barium salts—where the radium is the micro-component in the mixture of barium and radium salts—had taught many lessons about enriching a mixture with radium. But the conclusions about the natural laws involved diverged widely, depending on the methods that had been used. My collaborators (among whom N. Riehl, H. Käding, O. Erbacher, R. Mumbrauer, and Vera Senftner should be mentioned) studied the processes very carefully and discovered when homogeneous crystals formed and when nonhomogeneous crystals were to be expected.

During these investigations we found many examples that seemed to contradict my statement that joint precipitation will always produce mixed crystals. We found precipitation that looked like mixed crystals when we were dealing with components that could not form mixed crystals. We concluded that in these cases the micro-component had formed "anomalistic" mixed crystals in the lattice of the macro-component.

An interesting example of such anomalistic mixed crystals is the inclusion of lead, in the form of the lead isotopes thorium-B or radium-D, in crystallizing barium chloride. The inclusion of the lead isotopes follows Nernst's rule, but barium chloride forms monoclinic crystals while those of lead chloride are rhomboid. We found that crystallizing barium bromide did not accept the lead isotopes. Because of this difference between barium chloride and barium bromide one can, when enriching barium salts with radium, leave the radium-D (lead) with the radium, or separate it from the radium if it has already formed. To accomplish the former, one uses barium-radium chloride; to accomplish the latter one works with the bromides.

Another such example is the inclusion of thorium-B (lead) in sodium chloride, potassium chloride, and potassium bromide. The active micro-component will be strongly enriched in the crystallizing alkali metal salts and the distribution coefficient that is characteristic for the formation of mixed crystals remains remarkably constant during the whole process of crystallization. The alkaline salts form a lattice like that of rock salt, while lead chloride and lead bromide form rhomboid crystals. But if lead is added to the active micro-component, the three salts show a different behavior. Potassium chloride will accept a fair amount of normal inactive lead in its crystal lattice, potassium bromide will accept a lesser amount, and sodium chloride very little. Special experiments have shown that the lead does not enter the lattice as a lead-cation, but as a complex alkali-lead-anion.

Cesium chloride will not accept thorium-B in its lattice, a typical difference between various kinds of lattices which makes it logical to speak of mixed crystals—anomalistic mixed crystals—in the case of the rock-salt type of lattice.

My collaborators extended this research work in various directions and found a whole group of new phenomena—for example, the inclusion of the micro-component in interior adsorption systems which have to be strictly distinguished from the normal processes of adsorption. Details of the experimental work have been described in *Applied Radiochemistry* (pages 90–130).

Before concluding the discussion of joint precipitation and mixed crystals, I must also mention the explanation for the known but puzzling helium content of rock salt and potassium chloride and the fruitless searches for an inactive radium and the unknown element eka-cesium.

About lead and helium in rock salt

As has been reported, we found that alkali-halogenous compounds which crystallize from solutions containing lead chloride in the presence of rock salt will deposit noticeable amounts of lead in the salt crystals, even though the alkali-halogenous compounds and lead chloride are not isomorphous. I called such crystals anomalous mixed crystals; but they were not merely a scientific curiosity. Their existence led to some interesting conclusions about the lead and helium content of the North German salt deposits that are the result of the evaporation of ancient seas.

Since sea water contains tiny amounts of radium it must also contain the final products of radioactive decay—that is to say, lead—and the intermediate product radium-D, a lead isotope. When sea water evaporates, calcium carbonate is deposited first, carrying the radium and lead along with it. Uranium and thorium still remain in the solution. Gypsum, which is precipitated along with the calcium carbonate, does not carry radium or lead. Then the rest of the water evaporates, leaving sodium chloride and potassium chloride behind. Of course the lead, end product of the decay of uranium and radium, is still present, and since we found that lead enters into the crystals of sodium chloride and potassium chloride, these salts must contain lead. We proved that this is the case. One kilogram of alkaline rock salt always contains a few tenths of a milligram of lead. The mineral called carnallite, as well as potassium-magnesium-chloride, neither of which admitted lead into its crystals in the laboratory, were also found to be free of lead in nature.

The concentrated solutions of the evaporating sea water contained not only inactive lead, but also the radioactive lead isotope radium-D. This also entered the crystals of sodium chloride and of potassium chloride and was not accepted by carnallite—like inactive lead. Radium-D has a half-life of 22 years, decaying into polonium which emits alpha particles— that is, it produces helium. This explained the known but not understood fact that the salt of the North German rock salt deposits contained small but indubitably present amounts of helium. At the same time our findings explained why carnallite did not contain helium.

The strange anomalous mixed crystals which we had discovered in the course of our radiochemical work thus provided the solution to a puzzle posed by large-scale chemical events in nature.

The search for an "inactive radium" and for eka-cesium

The reasoning behind the search for an inactive or only weakly active radium began with a comparison with the rather stable heavy elements, uranium and thorium, which are found in about the same quantities in nature as their lower homologues, wolfram and hafnium. And since radium has an even atomic number, and since even-numbered elements are usually more stable and also more abundant than their odd-numbered neighbors, it did seem plausible to look for a stable radium (or "eka-barium") in barium salts. After all, the work that had been done for the purpose of extracting active radium from barium salts had showed the best methods for enriching a solution with radium salts. I asked a chemical factory to convert several hundred kilograms of "witherite" (barium carbonate) into barium bromide, and 270 kilograms of it were subjected to fractional crystallization. Having concentrated the 270 kilograms into 40 milligrams, we expected from our earlier experience with radium that we should have about 500,000 times as much eka-barium in our sample as would be found in the same quantity of the original salts. But when Dr. Donat of the Kaiser Wilhelm Institute checked the sample by spectrum analysis he could not find any lines indicating the presence of radium. The barium minerals contained less than 10^{-10} grams of the assumed eka-barium per gram of barium—in other words, this substance did not exist.

A similar experiment in search of an assumed eka-cesium was also carried out. The idea that this might exist was not as far-fetched as it may seem. Of course it was interesting to look for an element with the atomic number 87. Even though odd-numbered elements are less abundant than even-numbered elements, the possibility of its existence could not be denied.

Since the assumed eka-cesium was likely to form mixed crystals with cesium salts, we tried to prove the existence of the unknown element by way of a subsidiary reaction of large quantities of the actinium isotope mesothorium-2, or of the emanations radon and thoron. The first possibility consisted of finding alpha-particle emission of mesothorium-2; the second of finding a weak beta radiation of the emanation. The result was negative. A mesothorium-radium preparation yielded, after removal of all known radium and mesothorium products, a cesium-platinum chloride with an activity that was equivalent to 1/10,000,000 of the original activity. Therefore the possibility of a side chain producing eka-cesium was hardly more than 1/100,000,000 to 1, calculated from the activity of mesothorium-2, relative to the activity of the original mesothorium-radium preparations.

Of course, after the experiment with mesothorium-2 resulted negatively, it would have been an obvious idea to test actinium (or even mesothorium-2) for the emission of alpha particles, meaning a subsidiary reaction of the beta-emitting transformations. Strangely enough I never made that experiment, though in my earlier work I had never succeeded in obtaining a truly inactive actinium. I did not trust my methods of purification. At a later date (in 1939) the French researcher Mademoiselle M. Perey was both more knowledgeable and luckier. She was able to demonstrate that 1 percent of the atoms of actinium, by emitting an alpha particle, form an isotope of eka-cesium; element no. 89 becomes element no. 87. The new substance has a half-life of 21 minutes, and then, by emitting beta rays, becomes the long-known actium-X. Mademoiselle Perey first named the substance actinium-K, but later she gave it the more beautiful name of francium.

The indicator method

The indicator method is based on the idea that strongly active or otherwise easily recognizable isotopes can be used to detect the presence of inactive or weakly active elements in dilute concentrations where the normal chemical methods cannot be used. This method was developed by von Hévésy and Paneth during the year 1913 and had found a fairly wide application, even at a time when there were no artificially active radioisotopes of ordinary elements.

Ever since it became possible to make radioactive isotopes of almost all chemical elements with almost any desired degree of activity, the indicator method has become an indispensable tool of chemical, biochemical, and biological research, especially with the aid of the active carbon-14. Here I can only mention this field; while I was working in radiochemistry, artificially radioactive isotopes had not yet been discovered. But a few examples of the uses of radioactive isotopes, both natural and artificial, may be given.

It had been impossible to detect any radiation from actinium (element no. 89). But the actinium isotope called mesothorium-2, resulting from the decay of the radium isotope called mesothorium-1, was easily detected. It radiates both beta and gamma rays of high penetration, has the convenient half-life of 6.2 hours, and was therefore a perfect "indicator" for the nonradiating actinium-89. Continuing some work first begun by Madame Curie in 1929, we studied the "enrichment" of actinium in actinium-lanthanum mixtures and found, as the first publications by Madame Curie and S. Rosenblum in 1931 showed, that fractional precipitation of lanthanum-actinium oxalates from solutions in nitric acid was very successful. We used this method later to prove that the isotopes of alkaline earth metals which formed when uranium was bombarded with neutrons turned into lanthanum and not into actinium, which proved in turn that they were isotopes of barium and not of radium.

The use of alpha-radiating protactinium as an indicator for the isomer uranium-Z, which I had discovered, has already been mentioned in the discussion of uranium-Z. Of course this beta-radiating protactinium isotope could also be used, especially for the experimental verification of the half-life of protactinium. This work was carried out by my collaborator Ernst Walling; a fairly detailed discussion of his very careful and thorough work will be of interest.

When protactinium was found by Lise Meitner and me in 1917, we tried to make a preliminary determination of its half-life. One method consisted of separating recently formed protactinium from uranium preparations which should be as old as possible—we had some with minimum ages of 20, 52, and 60 years. We found a median value of 12,000 years for the half-life but had to call it a minimum value—partly because the ages of our uranium preparations were minimum ages and partly because we could not be sure that the uranium preparations had actually been completely free of protactinium when they were first made.

After I discovered the protactinium isotope uranium-Z, there was a possibility of utilizing this beta-radiating isotope as an indicator for protactinium and thereby repeating the determination of the half-life under conditions that left no room for doubt. The formation of protactinium from uranium was again to be determined, using uranium salts purified for the purpose. Any protactinium that might be present was removed by way of chemical separation with the addition of the indicator uranium-Z. This done, Walling had three batches of uranium salts that were certain to be free of protactinium. The material was uranyl nitrate; each batch weighed several kilograms. After 3.6 to 4 years had gone by, the protactinium that had formed in the meantime was separated from the uranium, again using uranium-Z as the indicator.

The procedure was about as follows: A carefully measured amount of uranium-Z was added to the uranium solution that was to be analyzed for protactinium. Both the protactinium and the uranium-Z were then chemically separated. The yield of beta-radiating substances (the value for uranium-Z being known) indicates the amount of protactinium that had been formed in a known time interval and also its half-life.

On the assumption that the alpha activity of protactinium is 3 percent that of uranium-I (we called this the "branching ratio"), Walling found a value of 20,000 years. Corroboration of our half-life value was furnished by von Grosse in 1928. He compared the alpha activity of protactinium (he was the first to obtain the pure substance from the minerals) with that of an equal weight of uranium. At a later date (1932) von Grosse improved his determination of the half-life of protactinium and arrived at the still-valid figure of 32,000 years.

Our figure of 20,000 years had been calculated on the assumption of a branching ratio of 3 percent. Later this ratio was found to be 4.6 percent; using this value in Walling's calculation the half-life becomes 30,600 years, in fine agreement with von Grosse's later value of 32,000 years. The quantities of protactinium which Walling had separated from 5 million uranium-activity units amounted to only 11 to 12 units, which shows the reliability of both the indicator method and the researcher.

Another example of the use of uranium-Z as an indicator for protactinium will be discussed later when we deal with the neutron bombardment of uranium. The problem was whether the artificial isotope(s) created by Enrico Fermi belonged to element no. 93, as he assumed, or to element no. 91—that is, protactinium. By using natural uranium as an indicator, a beta-radiating substance with a half-life of 23 minutes, derived from uranium by neutron bombardment, could be ascertained to be an artificial isotope of uranium. This showed that Fermi was right and this particular artificial isotope was indubitably the mother substance of a true transuranian element—namely, no. 93. Because of Fermi's investigations, we felt compelled to regard two other artificial isotopes of very short half-life as uranium isotopes; but they were not (see Chapter Seven, pages 140–46).

The Emanation Method

The research method that I shall now discuss could be considered a variation of the indicator method in the sense that here also an observable substance serves to indicate another factor. But the radioactive noble gas—either thoron or radon—does not serve as an indicator for an isotope of thorium or radium. Instead, it serves as an indicator of surface areas and changes in surface areas of small amounts of substances in which such an emanation is produced by thorium-X or radium. Like the discovery of radioactive recoil, the emanation method is the result of an early erroneous interpretation of certain experimental results.

Prior to the discovery of isotopes by Frederick Soddy and the resulting realization that the number of chemical elements between hydrogen and uranium cannot be greater than 92, many researchers had announced "new chemical elements" which later turned out to be merely isotopes. Lise Meitner and I, in the course of our work on beta rays did not hesitate to assume that we had discovered a new element if its behavior corroborated our idea that a single element could emit only one kind of radiation, either alpha or beta. Since we found that beta rays were emitted by thorium-X as well as by radium, in addition to the alpha-ray emission that had been known for a long time, we were forced to conclude that these elements were not pure but were mixtures of elements, and so subdivided them into thorium-X_1 and thorium-X_2, and, logically, into radium and radium-X. In fact, we took the beta-ray emission as a proof for our assumption that there was a radium-X. In the course of my radiochemical investigations I had measured beta-ray activities in deposits of ferric hydroxide containing radium. After several weeks such beta-ray emission should strike a balance with radon, the emanation of radium, and should then be stable. But changes continued to take place and several months later the deposits showed a higher intensity. I therefore concluded that this was due to a fairly long-lived and so far undiscovered radium-X, which was being formed constantly. Compared to these high hopes for a new element, the true explanation was trivial. At first the iron compound had a large surface and the radon being formed escaped to the outside. But then the hydroxide changed; its surface area grew smaller and smaller. Naturally more radon remained inside the preparation and its activity increased.

But observing and understanding this change was the take-off point for a new method of research which I named the emanation method, and which proved to be very fruitful in many ways in the years to come. Changes in the surface areas of originally large-surfaced substances could be followed; other changes could be caused by increasing the temperature; changes in crystalline structure could be checked, and also the gradual chemical breakdown of complex salts.

Let me describe some researches in which the emanation method was used.[6]

If radiothorium, thorium-X, or radium is evenly distributed in the substance to be investigated, the rate of release of the thoron or radon permits conclusions as to changes taking place in the substance. The term "emanation capability" was introduced to express the ratio of the amount of gas released to the amount of gas formed. Preparations with a large surface area have a high emanation capability, while those with a relatively small surface area, such as crystallized deposits, have a very low emanation capability. If the surface area undergoes changes (caused in the previous example of ferric hydroxide by drying out, followed by slow recrystallization) the emanation capability drops. Changes in a crystallized deposit which increase the surface area also increase the emanation capability.

When hydrates of iron and thorium are precipitated with small amounts of radiothorium at normal temperatures, their emanation capability amounts to 80 or even 90 percent. If these preparations are kept in air that is not too dry they age quite slowly. Such preparations are especially useful for obtaining very thin layers of an active deposit of thorium-B on a negatively charged electrode; because of thorium-B's convenient half-life of 10.6 hours they proved their worth as

[6] *Author's Note.* For my work up to 1934, see *Applied Radiochemistry* (*op. cit.*), which also contains a description of the various methods of measurement.

indicators of the formation of lead. When heated, strongly emanating deposits undergo characteristic structural changes which are clearly indicated by the changes in emanation capability.

In addition to strongly emanating radiothorium preparations, J. Heidenhain obtained deposits of ferrous compounds containing radium which had an emanation capability of 100 percent—even eight years later it was still above 92 percent.

Later Fritz Strassmann made strongly emanating preparations that were salts of long-chain fatty acids. He checked on the emanation capability of the barium salts of fatty acids as a function of the length of the molecular chains and obtained the following results.

Table 3   *The emanation capability of various barium salts*

barium salt	Percentage of emanation capability
acetate	3–4
propionate	17–18
butyrate	60–65
capronate	96
palmitate	100

Astonishingly enough, the corresponding salts which produce thoron instead of radon have almost the same emanation capability; since the half-life of thoron is less than 1 minute, such diffusion is quite surprising.

Other experiments with radiothorium or thorium-X involved the radioactive labeling of glasses of different compositions and thorium deposits obtained from solution of differing ages. The high resistance of Jena glass, compared with other types of glass that slowly corroded, and the slow formation of crystals in deposits from old thorium solutions could both be followed exactly. Using the method of Strassmann's experiments with fatty acids, T. Bjerge later found a neon isotope (neon-23) with a half-life of 40 seconds in an emanating sodium stearate that had been irradiated with neutrons.

From the behavior of strongly emanating preparations at normal temperatures, we proceeded to the study of substances with small surface areas at elevated temperatures and found that the emanation method permitted a large variety of successful investigations. Experiments carried out by Tammann showed at what temperature the crystal lattice begins to weaken. In the case of crystallized salts and oxides this is roughly one-half the temperature at which the substance will melt. The weakening

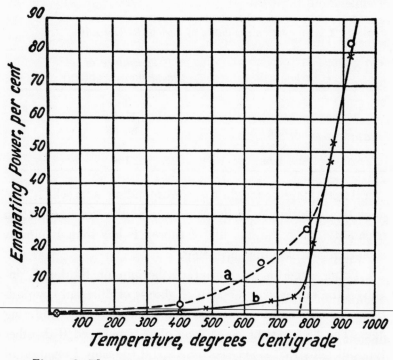

Figure 6. The emanating power of barium sulfate at increasing temperatures

of the lattice can easily be discovered by the emanation method.

Figure 6 shows the behavior of active barium sulfates at increasing temperatures. Before the experiment, one of the two samples had been dried out at a temperature of 110° centigrade; the other had been heated to red heat. Both curves show that the emanation capability is very low at first. The sulfate that had only been dried out (broken line) shows a faster increase in emanation capability than the sulfate that had been heated to a high temperature (solid line). The reason is that the "dry" sulfate still contained small amounts of water, the release of which is indicated by a higher release of emanation. Between 700° and 800° centigrade both curves rise sharply and the emanation capability soon reaches 90 percent. The maximum change takes place at around 770° centigrade—just about half the melting point of 1360° centigrade. Both preparations, after cooling, again showed the very low emanation capability of the crystallized salt.

Measurement of physical changes

Some of the most interesting investigations were those in which structural changes caused by elevated temperatures could be proved and studied—such as the investigations by K. E. Zimens into changes of the structure of various carbonates of alkaline-earth metals.

Figure 7 shows the changes in calcite and aragonite (that is, hexagonal and rhomboid calcium carbonate) when these are precipitated with small quantities of thorium-X. The salts were gradually heated in a carbon-dioxide atmosphere and the amount of released emanation was measured. At low temperatures the emanation capability of calcite is low and does not rise proportionately to the temperature, but after 600° centi-

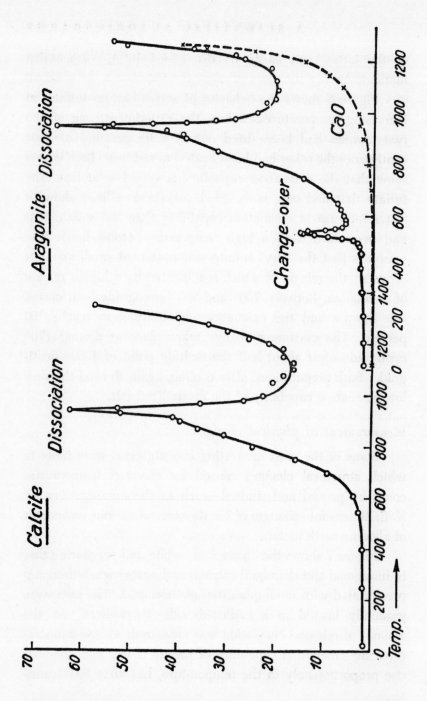

Figure 7. The emanating power of the two forms of CaCO₃ at increasing temperatures. (Emanating power is expressed in percentages.)

grade has been reached, the curve rises sharply. When aragonite is treated in the same manner, the results are the same up to 450°, then the curve rises sharply, reaching a peak at about 500° and then descends quickly. At about 600° the curve rises again, and after that change is the same as that of calcite for the same temperatures. Evidently the aragonite turned into calcite at 500°. Renewed heating after cooling shows only the calcite curve; the change at 500° is a nonreversible monotropic change, as could also be shown by Debye-Scherrer photographs.

At 600° Tammann's temperature for the weakening of the crystal lattice is reached, and just above 900° there is a high peak marking the dissociation of the carbonate. At that point carbon dioxide is freed and carries the accumulated emanation along with it. What is now left is calcium oxide; the second sharp peak of the curve indicates the weakening of its crystal lattice.

K. E. Zimens also made a thorough investigation of the behavior of barium and strontium carbonates during heating. At first the curves showed many different shapes; because the crystals varied in size according to the method used to produce them, the investigation showed that these carbonates also changed from a rhomboid to a hexagonal lattice.

Continuing this work, H. Kallweit used the emanation method to investigate the changes taking place in mixed crystals of calcium carbonate and strontium carbonate with varying proportions of the two salts. At a specific proportion the monotropic change of the aragonite into the enantiotrope of the strontianite could be clearly observed.

Measurement of chemical changes

Many chemical compounds, especially those salts containing crystal water, undergo a gradual dehydration when heated, and this process can be followed by using the emanation method. C. Lieber, who worked with halogen compounds of barium, has shown that emanation is expelled in clearly defined stages. One of the best examples of those changes is the gradual conversion of barium oxalate into barium carbonate, which proceeds in a number of definite steps. Figure 8 shows

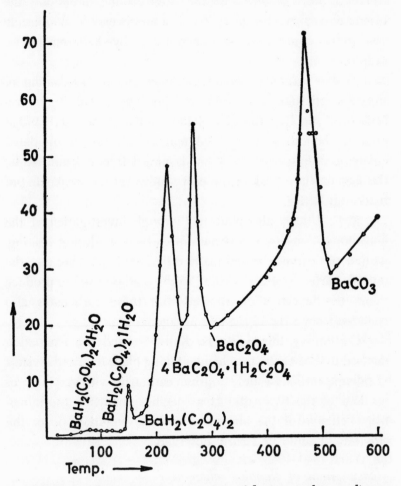

Figure 8. The successive conversions of barium oxalate, ending as barium carbonate. (Emanating power is expressed in percentages.)

134

the curve of emanation release during the various stages of the chemical conversion.

O. Werner of my Institute then extended the emanation method to the study of metals containing radium. As the scope of the investigations was extended, the equipment was also systematically improved. H. J. Born adopted it for the detection of very rapid changes, while K. E. Zimens developed a fully automatic registering apparatus which superseded the earlier measurements with electroscopes. S. Flügge and Zimens, in addition to their experimental work, were also concerned with theory; they published a comprehensive report on the determination of particle sizes and diffusion constants in the *Zeitschrift für Physikalische Chemie* (1939, pages 179–220). In 1942, Zimens published in the same journal a complete survey of the actual applications of the emanation method. The first part of his survey dealt with the steady improvement in the laboratory methods used and included a complete bibliography of the emanation method, listing eighty-one original contributions and ten surveys. The second part covered the analysis of the measurements obtained (*ibid.*, 1942, pages 1–51 and 95–128).

Somewhat related to our experiments in detecting changes in surface areas by the emanation method is a report by K. Starke (1937) entitled: "Investigation of the Surface Areas of Mixtures of Catalysts and the Changes in Surface Areas Caused by Solid-State Reactions."

Wilhelm Schröder published a whole series of interesting reports of solid-state reactions and their investigation by the emanation method in the *Zeitschrift für Elektrochemie* during the years 1940–1948. He investigated the weakening of the crystal lattices of metallic oxides and especially the reactions of metal oxides with a valence of 2 or 3 that lead to the formation of spinel. The emanation method enabled him to follow the structural changes that accompanied these reactions. But I must forego a detailed discussion of these last experiments since they were not carried out at the Kaiser Wilhelm Institute.

SEVEN

At the Kaiser Wilhelm Institute for Chemistry—1933 to 1945: Work with Artificially Radioactive Isotopes

Neutron Bombardment of Uranium and Thorium—with Lise Meitner and Fritz Strassmann

It was in 1919 that Rutherford succeeded for the first time in producing a change in the nucleus of an atom. He bombarded nitrogen atoms with alpha particles—that is, helium nuclei—by exposing the atoms to a highly active preparation of radium. Rutherford proved that a very small number of nitrogen atoms were changed into oxygen atoms (of the isotope oxygen-17) with release of a proton or hydrogen nucleus. He recognized the hydrogen by the higher penetration of the proton as compared to that of the alpha particle. Blackett checked the nuclear reaction by means of photographs of a Wilson cloud chamber; in 20,000 photographs he found 8 in which the path of the alpha particle could be seen to end and that of a proton begin.

The equation for this reaction was therefore:

$$_7N^{14} + {}_2He^4 \rightarrow {}_8O^{17} + {}_1H^1$$

Rutherford calculated that it would take several millennia to produce 1 cubic millimeter of hydrogen with his radiation source.

The fundamental discovery of artificially induced changes in the atomic nucleus was only the beginning of a long line of other discoveries. Nuclear changes could be caused in other elements too, but only in elements with a comparatively weak electric charge in the nucleus—up to argon and potassium—because nuclei with greater charges repelled the alpha particles so strongly that they could not penetrate into the interior of the nucleus even when they scored a direct hit.

The year 1932 brought the discoveries of the positron (also called the positive electron), of deuterium or heavy hydrogen, and of the neutron. The neutron, which was discovered by Sir James Chadwick in England, has the same mass as the hydrogen atom but does not carry an electric charge; it was discovered by bombarding beryllium with alpha particles:

$$_4Be^{10} + {}_2He^4 \rightarrow {}_0n^1 + {}_6C^{13}$$

Two years later Frédéric and Irène Joliot-Curie discovered additional neutron-producing reactions. Bombarding boron and aluminum with alpha particles also produced neutrons, but the resulting isotopes were radioactive. In the process radioactive nitrogen and radioactive phosphorus were also discovered.[1]

[1] *Author's Note.* The asterisks in the equations that follow indicate that the particular isotope is radioactive.

$$_5B^{10} + {}_2He^4 \rightarrow {}_7N^{*13} + {}_0n^1; \quad {}_7N^{*13} \xrightarrow[\text{10 min.}]{\beta^+} {}_6C^{13}$$

$$_{13}Al^{27} + {}_2He^4 \rightarrow {}_{15}P^{*30} + {}_0n^1; \quad {}_{15}P^{*30} \xrightarrow[\text{2.2 min.}]{\beta^+} {}_{15}Si^{30}$$

This was the discovery of artificial radioactivity!

The newly discovered neutron opened the way for stormy developments in nuclear research. As a result atomic energy can now be used for peaceful purposes and many artificial isotopes of any desired activity can be made in such quantities that they can be used in ordinary chemistry. But among the results are also the atom bomb and the hydrogen bomb!

Fermi's eka-rhenium, element no. 93.

It took four years for scientists to explain what actually takes place when uranium is bombarded with neutrons. Because of this delay in finding the true interpretation, the ideas that Lise Meitner, Fritz Strassmann, and I advanced about the artificial isotopes all turned out to be wrong. We thought them to be transuranian elements—elements with an atomic number higher than 92. Everyone else who had worked on the problem had arrived at the same conclusion; there seemed to be no other.

A review of our admittedly faulty reasoning is still interesting and instructive, since it also explains the delay in arriving at the truth.

Enrico Fermi was the first to call attention to the importance of neutron bombardment. He pointed out that neutrons, since they carry no electric charge, can penetrate into the atomic nucleus without being repelled by its positive charge. As a consequence of this reasoning, Fermi and his collaborators bombarded virtually all the elements of the Periodic Table. Since the nuclei captured the neutrons, radioactive isotopes of the elements they irradiated were obtained. These new isotopes decayed by emitting beta particles (electrons) and became atoms of the next-higher element. The Italian researchers systematically went up all the way to uranium, the element with the highest atomic number then known. From uranium they obtained beta-emitting substances with short half-lives—10 seconds, 40 seconds, 13 minutes, and 90 minutes. The first two could not be chemically separated from uranium because they did not exist long enough; reasoning by analogy from the behavior of middle-weight elements they were believed to be isotopes created by neutron capture. In short, they were thought to be artificial isotopes formed by uranium nuclei. However, since they emitted beta particles, Fermi concluded that they had to be isotopes of elements beyond uranium. Therefore, either the 13-minute and the 90-minute isotopes were both isotopes of element no. 93, or else results of a decay chain from element no. 93 (eka-rhenium, the 13-minute isotope) to element no. 94 (eka-osmium, the 90-minute substance). However, A. von Grosse, who, ten years earlier, had succeeded in isolating protactinium at my Institute, doubted Fermi's interpretation. Grosse thought it more probable that the 13-minute isotope (which was better known than any of the others) was an isotope of the next-lower element, protactinium. Ida Noddack went further; she suggested that *all* the elements of the periodic system would have to be eliminated before one could claim to have found a transuranian element. Her suggestion was so out of line with the then-accepted ideas about the atomic nucleus that it was never seriously discussed. The only question seemed to be whether Fermi had found isotopes of transuranian elements, or isotopes of the next-lower element, protactinium.

At that time Lise Meitner and I decided to repeat Fermi's experiments in order to find out whether the 13-minute isotope was a protactinium isotope or not. It was a logical decision; having been the discoverers of protactinium, we knew its chemical characteristics, and my beta-emitting protactinium isotope uranium-Z was a fine "indicator" because of its convenient 6.2-hour half-life. Using the indicator method, we established that Fermi's 13-minute isotope certainly was not an isotope of protactinium. Hence we concluded that Fermi must be correct, and the 13-minute substance was an element with a nuclear charge of 93—eka-rhenium.

The transuranian series

After the controversy between von Grosse and Fermi had been settled in Fermi's favor, we started our own work on neutron bombardment of uranium and also of thorium. These investigations covered a period of four years and were published in twenty original papers. From 1935 to 1938 practically all the work was done in collaboration with Fritz Strassmann. The proper explanation for the observed phenomena was not found until 1938.

How could we possibly have remained in the dark for so long?

Enrico Fermi's work on many of the elements of the periodic system seemed to show clearly just what happened when an atomic nucleus captured a neutron. The nucleus, which had grown by one neutron—that is, by one unit of mass—emitted beta rays, and this beta-ray emission increased the electric charge of the nucleus by one unit; this was a kind of adjustment to the fact that the new higher mass failed to correspond to the electric charge. Fermi had also found that the nuclear reactions increased in number if the neutrons had been slowed down by collision with the hydrogen atoms in hydrogen-rich substances, such as water, paraffin, and others. We also worked with slow neutrons and the process seemed simplicity itself: via emission of beta rays the next-higher element in the periodic system was formed.

Others, knowing about Fermi's and our own work, used fast neutrons, highly accelerated protons, and alpha particles (helium nuclei) and also obtained changes in the nuclei of the substances that were bombarded. But in all cases these changes seemed to follow a simple law: the positive charge of the bombarded nucleus either remained the same or was changed by one unit either way—in rare instances by two units plus or minus. The new products, therefore, always fell into the immediate neighborhood of the irradiated elements, which simplified their chemical identification. The loss of a larger portion of the nucleus—a loss larger than an alpha particle—seemed to be outside the range of any reasonable discussion, especially when neutrons of low energy were used. This was the point of view of nuclear physics and prior to 1938 nothing happened to compel anybody to move away from this position.

Continuing our experimental research on Fermi's 13-minute substance, which we also called eka-rhenium because of its suspected position in the periodic system vertically below rhenium, we began to pay attention to the 90-minute substance. At first, it was not clear whether this was an isotope of the 13-minute substance or the product of the transformation of that substance. We succeeded in separating them chemically and therefore concluded that the 90-minute body was the transformation product of the 13-minute body, and hence an isotope of element no. 94 —that is, eka-osmium. But we soon found that the 90-minute body was not a homogeneous substance; we found a substance with a half-life of 59 minutes and a few others, some with longer and some with much shorter half-lives. The findings grew more complicated all the time, and the difficulty of sorting out the many different substances discovered increased at the same rate. It was difficult to think of a plausible system. The one thing that was definite was that the starting point was always an artificial uranium isotope.

The products—all of them beta-ray emitters—therefore had to be considered without exception as elements beyond uranium —eka-rhenium, eka-osmium, eka-iridium, and eka-platinum. In each case there were two substances, apparently identical chemically and approximately equal in radiation intensity. Disregarding the natural uranium isotope of mass 235 because it was much too rare, we decided that all the new substances must start with uranium-238. But this forced us to assume that the reactions could take place in two different chains of isomers, one of which could be followed to a beta-emitting eka-platinum, and the other to eka-osmium, perhaps even to eka-iridium. In two comprehensive reports we discussed the chemical results and also the physical problems; one of these was published in the *Reports* of the German Chemical Society, the other in the *Zeitschrift für Physik*.

The report on the chemical properties was subdivided as follows:

    I. The (chemical) differences of all transuranian elements (nos. 93–96) from uranium and the neighboring lower elements.

   II. Chemical proof for the existence of the artificial isotopes of uranium.

  III. The differences between eka-rhenium (no. 93) and the homologues of the platinum metals (nos. 94, 95, 96).

  IV. The differences between the homologues of the platinum metals:

1. The separation of eka-osmium (no. 94) from eka-iridium (no. 95).
2. The separation of eka-platinum (no. 96) from the other homologues of the platinum metals (nos. 95 and 94).
V. Similarities and differences between the transuranian elements and their lower homologues rhenium and the platinum metals.

We conceived the following two chains of nuclear reactions, to the second of which is added a substance with a half-life of about 60 days which was not discovered until 1938, after the original publication, and which we tentatively called eka-iridium. The two chains were:

$$(1) \quad {}_{92}U + \cdot n \rightarrow ({}_{92}U + n) \xrightarrow[10 \text{ sec.}]{\beta} {}_{93}\text{Eka-Re} \xrightarrow[2.2 \text{ min.}]{\beta}$$

$$ \quad {}_{94}\text{Eka-Os} \xrightarrow[59 \text{ min.}]{\beta} {}_{95}\text{Eka-Ir} \xrightarrow[66 \text{ h.}]{\beta} {}_{96}\text{Eka-Pt} \xrightarrow[2.5 \text{ h.}]{\beta} {}_{97}\text{Eka-Au?}$$

$$(2) \quad {}_{92}U + \cdot n \rightarrow ({}_{92}U + n) \xrightarrow[40 \text{ sec.}]{\beta} {}_{93}\text{Eka-Re} \xrightarrow[16 \text{ min.}]{\beta} {}_{94}\text{Eka-Os}$$

$$ \quad \xrightarrow[5.7 \text{ h.}]{\beta} {}_{95}\text{Eka-Ir?} \xrightarrow[60 \text{ d.}]{\beta}$$

Since all the substances mentioned could be precipitated with hydrogen sulfide from acid solutions and their chemical characteristics were reasonably compatible with those of the homologous platinum metals, no one criticized the scheme.

It took years to find out that the real transuranium elements, discovered mainly by Americans after the fission of uranium atoms had been established, are not chemical analogues to the platinum metals at all but form a group of elements that correspond to the lanthanids. Both Niels Bohr and V. M. Goldschmidt had suggested that a number of elements analogous to the lanthanids might begin with uranium or with thorium, but for the reasons mentioned, including the chemical tests, we had to consider our substances as true homologues of the platinum metals and on that assumption our tentative names were justified.

In the second report, which covered the physical aspects of our work, we tried to calculate the effective cross section for the assumed neutron-capture reactions. It was found to be the same for both chains; and the value found "proved" that only uranium-238 could be activated by neutron captures. The rare uranium-235 was disregarded.

An artificial uranium isotope with a 23-minute half-life

The two chain reactions described in the preceding section could be caused by fast neutrons, but the use of neutrons slowed down by the presence of hydrogen gave better results. In additions to these two chain reactions, we obtained still another substance which was produced only by fairly slow neutrons with a definite energy—in other words, by a resonance process. This was a uranium isotope with a half-life of 23 minutes. In this case definite chemical proof could be obtained that it was indeed a uranium isotope. Fractional precipitation of the artificial isotope and of the irradiated uranium in the form of uranyl-sodium-acetate produced for the 23-minute substance the same activity for the first and the last fraction, if the amounts of uranium had the same weight.

Since this substance radiated beta particles, there could be no doubt that it would produce element no. 93, eka-rhenium. Because our preparations were weak we could not find the new element; we concluded that it must be a long-lived substance. But also we were not especially interested, because we believed that we already knew two isotopes of element no. 93, a 2-minute substance and a 16-minute substance, the products of Fermi's short-lived "uranium isotopes" with half-lives of 10 seconds and 40 seconds.

This mistake, of course, was due to the almost tragic confusion caused by accepting the 10-second and 40-second substances as isotopes of uranium. If we had not had Fermi's 13-minute substance (we corrected its half-life to 16 minutes) which resulted from one of the short-lived so-called uranium isotopes that seemed to represent element no. 93, we would have tried harder to find element no. 93 as the product of the 23-minute substance. This would not even have been difficult. By irradiating a larger quantity of uranium, or by repeatedly irradiating the same sample of uranium, we could have amassed ten times as much of the unknown substance and established its existence by means of a thin-walled Geiger counter. In addition to having been the discoverers of protactinium, the element to the left of uranium in the Periodic Table, we might also have discovered the element to the right of uranium.

Later, after the discovery of uranium fission, E. M. McMillan and P. H. Abelson did discover the product of the decay of the 23-minute substance and described its characteristics. The element, which they named neptunium, has a half-life of 2.3 days. (For more details, see pages 175–77.)

Summarizing the work on transuranian elements, it must be admitted that many carefully conducted investigations led to wrong conclusions. But nobody should be blamed. Fermi had no choice but to regard his short-lived substances as uranium isotopes. They resulted in numerous products, all of which seemed to have in their nuclei higher electric charges than that of uranium. Their chemical characteristics were compatible with those expected of higher homologues of the platinum metals, which is what the elements beyond uranium were considered at the time.

Suspicion should have been aroused by the fact that two of the "uranium isotopes" originated under irradiation conditions entirely different from those producing the 23-minute substance, which definitely was a uranium isotope, but the situation was so complicated that even this strange fact was accepted.

The Nonrecognized Fission of Thorium

Enrico Fermi and his collaborators had subjected thorium to neutron bombardment, as they had uranium, and had found two beta-ray-emitting substances with half-lives of about 1 minute and 24 minutes respectively.

We, too, starting at about the time we began work on uranium, had worked with thorium. Because of our weak neutron sources—we only had small radium-beryllium tubes with 500 to 1000 milligrams of radium—this work was especially painstaking when compared with that on uranium. A purified uranium preparation is a source of alpha rays only because the next link in the chain of transformations, uranium-X, has a half-life of 24 days. If the period of irradiation is not too long, when the fission products have been separated, only uranium-X and the original uranium need to be considered as radioactive elements. With thorium what is normally used is a mixture of thorium, mesothorium $(1 + 2)$, and thorium-X; their combined natural radioactivity is stronger by far than that of the weak artificial products. For Fermi and for other researches in the field this posed no problem because they had more powerful neutron sources. The activity of their artificial products was so great that small impurities consisting of the natural decay products of thorium hardly mattered.

The chief reason that I dared to experiment with thorium was that we had a quantity of natural thorium that had been cleansed over many years from the steadily forming mesothorium. This had been prepared because at one time in the past I had decided that I wanted to use pure thorium as an alpha-ray emitter. Mesothorium $(1 + 2)$ is the mother substance of radio-thorium, which cannot be separated chemically from thorium, since they are isotopes of the same element. But mesothorium can be separated from thorium, and if that is continuously re-moved, the radiothorium and all its products can gradually be made to disappear. Fritz Strassmann had performed the separa-tions for several years before we began irradiating thorium, and in 1935 we estimated that our thorium contained only about 1 percent of radiothorium. This figure of 1 percent refers, of course, to the percentage of radioactivity, not to the weight or volume of the substances. Having this preparation we felt that we could start neutron bombardment, especially since we had had experience in separation processes over many years.

Our very first attempt had an encouraging result; we found that the irradiation caused two process, one that could be inten-sified and another that could not.

We found that the process of producing Fermi's 1-minute substance cannot be intensified; it produces a substance with a half-life of about 11 minutes. The formation of Fermi's 24-min-ute substance can be intensified. However, we found a half-life of 30 minutes for this substance; all figures for half-lives were of course subject to some uncertainty. But we could show, in agreement with Fermi's results, that the 30-minute (formerly 24-minute) substance was an isotope of thorium. The 1-minute body was taken to be an isotope of radium and the following substance as an isotope of actinium. Experiments by Irène Joliot-Curie, H. von Halban, and P. Preiswerk corroborated this be-lief, and also added a new substance with a half-life of 3.5 hours which they could identify as an actinium isotope.

E. Rona and E. Neuninger also experimented with neutron

bombardment of thorium. Like us, they used a thorium preparation that had been freed of mesothorium; their preparation had been purified for fourteen years by Stefan Meyer of the Viennese Radium Institute. Rona and Neuninger corroborated our findings and also described another actinium isotope with a half-life of 24 hours. Irène Joliot-Curie, von Halban, and Preiswerk, working as a team, and Rona and Neuninger, also working as a team, suggested decay schemes that were different from ours and also described additional substances which we did not find. The neutron sources available to these researchers were also rather weak, so that relatively minor impurities, in addition to the natural decay products of thorium, made it difficult to determine half-lives and to understand the processes involved. The thorium used by Irène Joliot-Curie and her collaborators evidently contained a fairly high proportion of radiothorium, which made work even more difficult for them.

The results of our work on thorium were published in the *Zeitschrift für Physik* (vol. 109, pp. 538–552, 1938). The following equation referred to a process that could be intensified; the

$$_{90}\text{Th}^{232} + n \rightarrow {}_{90}\text{Th}^{233} \xrightarrow[26 \text{ min.}]{\beta^-} {}_{91}\text{Pa}^{233} \xrightarrow[25 \text{ days}]{\beta^-} {}_{92}\text{U}^{233}?$$

25-day substance mentioned in the equation was our discovery.

The following three schemes of decay were considered to be processes that could not be intensified:

$$_{90}\text{Th}^{232}(\text{n}, \alpha) \rightarrow {}_{88}\text{Ra}^{229} \xrightarrow[<1 \text{ min.}]{\beta^-} {}_{89}\text{Ac}^{229} \xrightarrow[\sim 18 \text{ min.}]{\beta^-} \text{Th ?}$$

$$_{90}\text{Th}^{232}(\text{n}, \alpha) \rightarrow {}_{88}\text{Ra}^{229} \xrightarrow[15 \text{ min.}]{\beta^-} {}_{89}\text{Ac}^{229} \xrightarrow[\sim 3.5 \text{ h.}]{\beta^-} \text{Th ?}$$

$$_{90}\text{Th}^{232}(\text{n}, \alpha) \rightarrow {}_{88}\text{Ra}^{229} \xrightarrow[\sim 4 \text{ h.}]{\beta^-} {}_{89}\text{Ac}^{229} \xrightarrow[20 \text{ to } 30 \text{ h.}]{\beta^-} \text{Th ?}$$

Assuming neutron capture and alpha-particle emission, we had three radium isotopes that changed into three actinium isotopes; the half-lives, as has been mentioned before, could only be considered approximately correct. The last sentence of our report read: "It was shown here for the first time that series of isomers will form by alpha-particle emission. The possibilities of isomer formation have been discussed."

We thus explained the appearance of radium isotopes by assuming an alpha-particle emission. But experiments designed to find alpha particles, carried out by G. von Droste, a member of our Institute, had failed.

Of course the facts were quite different, as was learned after the discovery of uranium fission. The supposed isotopes of radium and of actinium were actually isotopes of barium and lanthanum respectively. But at the time nobody doubted the results we had obtained and the conclusions we had reached, even though the existence of series of isomers was hard to admit theoretically.

A number of the artificial isotopes believed to be radium and actinium had been described by us (as well as Irène Joliot-Curie, von Halban, and Preiswerk) as early as 1935. If we had only tried to separate the radium from the carrier barium or the actinium from its carrier lanthanum, the fact of nuclear fission would have been recognized several years earlier.

Lise Meitner's Departure from Berlin

The paper about thorium and neutron bombardment mentioned in the preceding section had been submitted in May 1938 by Meitner, Hahn, and Strassmann. On July 10 we sent another report to the editor of *Die Naturwissenschaften*, in which we described still another transuranian element with a half-life of about 60 days. Its place in the table was still uncertain, though we guessed that it might be eka-iridium of transuranic sequence II. This was my last collaboration with Lise Meitner, after more than thirty years of working together, and her last work in Germany.

Being Austrian, Lise Meitner had not been subject to Hitler's anti-Jewish laws. But in the spring of 1938 when Austria became part of Germany, she was no longer protected by being a citizen of another country. Since she was "over 50 percent non-Aryan," the chances of keeping her in her position at the Institute grew smaller every day. Privy Councilor Bosch, then President of the Kaiser Wilhelm Society, attempted to obtain an exit visa for her but this was refused. Bosch had a private discussion with Lise Meitner and me, in which he told us about the letter from the Minister of Education. There was nothing else that Bosch could do toward enabling her to leave Germany.

Professor Scherrer in Zurich was asked to write to Professor Coster in Holland, and Professors Coster, Fokker, and de Haas persuaded the Dutch government to admit Lise Meitner without a visa. She succeeded in getting into Holland; then, through Niels Bohr, Professor Siegbahn in Stockholm offered her a position in that city, which she accepted.

Fritz Strassmann

The third member of our "transuranium group," Fritz Strassmann, was not molested or annoyed by the Hitler government. After the many scientific publications he had authored, some alone, some with me or with Lise Meitner, it was logical that he be made a Privatdozent at the University of Berlin in addition to his position at the Kaiser Wilhelm Institute. I suggested that he write to the University about his wish to enter academic life. He did, and was told that he must first join one of the National Socialist organizations. This he refused to do, and the University in turn refused him any position. But he was able to continue to work undisturbed in my Institute, since the various laws concerning higher education did not apply to us.

After the war Strassmann, like everybody else, received "restitution." He was appointed *Professor ordinarius* ["full professor"] for Inorganic Chemistry and Radiochemistry at the newly founded University of Mainz without having to go through any of the preliminary stages.

The So-called Radium Isotopes

The reader will remember the list (page 144) of the many so-called transuranian elements that seemingly were created by the bombardment of uranium with slow neutrons. In 1938 this list was lengthened by the addition of the newly discovered "60-day substance" which could not easily be fitted into our series, but which also seemed to be a transuranian element.

One year earlier, in 1937, Irène Joliot-Curie and P. Savitch had added another substance which complicated matters even more. They described it as a substance with a half-life of 3.5 hours and rather indefinite chemical characteristics. At first they thought it might be an isotope of thorium but as a result of a letter which Lise Meitner and I wrote them, they abandoned this idea. They then considered it to be an isotope of actinium. But fractional precipitation of the new substance with lanthanum as the carrier and the addition of a small amount of natural actinium proved that it could not be actinium. Chemically it rather resembled lanthanum. Irène Joliot-Curie and Savitch rather hesitantly concluded their report with the words:

"Il semble donc que ce corps ne puisse être qu'un élément

transuranien possédant des propriétés très différentes de celles des autres éléments transuranien connus, hypothèse qui soulève des difficultés d'interprétation."

In a later report they once more described their experiments relating to the chemical characteristics of the 3.5-hour substance. They stressed its chemical similarity with lanthanum but could not bring themselves to say that it actually was lanthanum:

"Dans l'ensemble, les propriétés de R 3.5 h. sont celles du lanthane, dont il semble jusqu'ici qu'on ne puisse le séparer que par fractionnement."

They then discussed a number of possibilities for inserting the 3.5-hour substance into the series of transuranian elements, admitting that these attempts were unsatisfactory and hard to understand. They were in the same difficult situation with lanthanum in which we soon afterward found ourselves to be with barium. Lanthanum suggested itself all the time, but such long jumps inside the Periodic Table were then believed to be impossible. In their final report (1938) they also stated that their 3.5-hour substance seemed to contain substances with longer half-lives, but they could determine neither the half-lives nor the chemical nature of the substances.

Since the substance discovered by Irène Joliot-Curie and Savitch was thought to be a transuranian element with unusual characteristics, we tried to obtain it ourselves in a thorough investigation. In addition to the hydrogen-sulfide precipitation which we used for all transuranian elements, we checked on other groups of analytical precipitations too. Using lanthanum as carrier as a representative of the rare earth elements, barium as carrier as a representative of the alkaline earth elements, and zirconium as carrier in still another set of experiments, we found a number of radioactive substances in our precipitates. The 3.5-hour substance we concluded to be a mixture of several substances, making its chemical nature very difficult to determine.

The experiments with barium were especially enlightening. In our very first report (*Die Naturwissenschaften;* vol. 26, p. 755, 1938), we stated that irradiation of uranium with neutrons produced, in addition to the transuranian elements, three active isotopes of radium. In this report we published three chain reactions, beginning with the beta-emitting radium isotopes and three resulting actinium isotopes. We gave the half-lives "in rough approximation" and pointed to the unexpected fact that all these processes could also be started with slow neutrons. It seemed absolutely necessary, therefore, to determine the chemical characteristics of all these newly discovered radioactive elements.

In January 1939 we published (*ibid.* vol. 27, pp. 11–15) a very thorough report: "On the Determination and Behavior of the Alkaline Earth Metals Resulting from Uranium Irradiated with Neutrons." In this report we gave an analysis of the "new radium isotopes, their half lives, and the resulting substances." Our conclusion—namely, that we had chains of isomers of radium isotopes—was based on the fact that these isotopes could be precipitated with barium and had all the characteristics of barium. We had succeeded in separating uranium, protactinium, thorium, and actinium; "hence, if we disregard the barium itself, only radium is left."

When we precipitated barium, the obvious idea was to use barium sulfate, which, except for barium chromate, is the least soluble of all the barium salts. But earlier experience and a few preliminary experiments had warned us against barium sulfate; we had learned that the sulfate carries small amounts of uranium and traces of thorium and actinium isotopes, and the precipitate therefore is impure. Fritz Strassmann suggested the use of barium chloride, precipitated with concentratic nitric acid. It forms beautiful little crystals, the purity of which we checked in a number of ways. Two of these may be mentioned.

We began with 10 grams of uranyl nitrate which had not been irradiated and which showed an activity of about 400,000 particles per minute; the precipitated barium chloride showed an activity of about 14 particles per minute.

The second test was begun with an actinium isotope (beta-radiating mesothorium-2) with an activity of about 2500 particles per minute; the precipitated barium chloride showed an activity of 3 particles per minute. We tested, in a similar manner, precipitates from irradiated uranium which contained the many transuranian elements, always obtaining fine results. Of course, when precipitating barium we could not immediately distinguish between barium isotopes and radium isotopes; but since barium was "out of the question," the substance could only be radium.

The main part of our second report (published in January 1939) dealt with the curves of activity of the "radium" isotopes produced by neutron bombardments of differing duration. This led to "definite" statements about the number of isotopes and their half-lives. We also gave approximate figures for the half-lives of the resulting "actinium" isotopes. But our position had changed somewhat: instead of the three isotopes of our first report we now assumed the existence of four, the fourth being a very short-lived radium isotope thought to be the mother substance of an actinium isotope with a half-life of less than 30 minutes.

The "Radium" Isotopes Were Barium

The report published in January 1939 dealt mainly with the analysis of the various "radium" isotopes, but it ended with something entirely new: the suggestion that the "radium" isotopes were really barium and not radium and the "actinium" isotopes were lanthanum. *This conclusion violated all previous experience in the field of nuclear physics!*

The last part of this report reads as follows:

We now have to discuss the results of some recent experiments which we publish with some reluctance because of their extraordinary results. In order to establish the chemical nature of the substances called "radium isotopes" beyond any doubt, we performed fractional crystallizations and fractional precipitations of the active barium salts of the type used for the enriching of barium salts with radium.

For enriching barium salts with radium during fractional crystallization barium bromide is used; barium chromate is even better for this purpose if the tiny crystals are not removed too soon. Barium chloride is enriched to a lesser extent than the bromide, while barium carbonate even works in the opposite direction, though only slightly. Such experiments when performed with our radioactive barium preparations always produced a negative result. *The radioactivity remained the same in all the fractions of barium;* at least within the limits of the possible error of our experimental methods. We then carried out a few fractionations with the radium isotope thorium-X and with mesothorium-1, also a radium isotope. They turned out precisely as one expected them to after much experience with radium. Then the indicator method was applied to a mixture of the long-lived radium-IV and pure radium-free mesothorium-1. The mixture, with barium bromide as the carrier, was fractionally crystallized. *Mesothorium-1 was enriched, but radium-IV was not.* Its activity remained the same if the barium content of the fractions was the same. We had to conclude that our "radium isotopes" have the chemical characteristics of barium. Speaking as chemists, we even have to say that these new substances are barium, not radium.

The report had been originally intended to describe the different radium isotopes and their radioactive decay and had originally borne the title: "On the Radium Isotopes Produced by the Neutron Bombardment of Uranium and Their Behavior." The final title contained the term "alkaline earth metals" instead of "radium isotopes." The change resulted from the experiments with fractional crystallizaion which indicated that barium was the same as our artificial radium. The indicator method had implied artificial radium and natural radium.

Having arrived at this result we began to wonder whether we should not use the term "barium isotopes" instead of "radium isotopes." But most of the report had been written, and it would have had to be rewritten completely, especially since in view of this result its major portion was not especially interesting any more. We wanted to publish as fast as possible, so we used the term "alkaline earth metals." We did not even wait for the final results of indicator experiments with long-lived isotopes. The final results were published in another report which we submitted in January 1939 (see Appendix I).

Fission of Uranium and Thorium

While the first report (published in 1938) was being written, we naturally gave much thought to the question of what really had taken place. We had to assume that the heavy uranium atom broke into several smaller pieces, so we subtracted the masses of the known barium isotopes from the mass of the uranium atom. The results were elements such as no. 43 (then still undiscovered, now known as technetium), ruthenium, rhodium, and palladium—in other words, the elements in the middle of the platinum group. These have chemical characteristics

157

which we thought could be reconciled with the chemical characteristics of our transuranian elements. Our mistake was, of course, in subtracting the masses of the atoms, instead of subtracting the atomic numbers—that is, the nuclear charges.

The correct explanation was published (*Nature,* vol. 143, p. 239, 1939), by Lise Meitner and O. R. Frisch, to whom we had communicated our results by letter before they were published. They, in turn, passed on their conclusions to Niels Bohr before their contribution saw print. Niels Bohr mentioned their results at a meeting of the American Physical Society on January 26, 1939, thus enabling several of the scientists present to repeat the experiment of uranium fission the same day, just ten days after Frisch had carried it out. Unfortunately, the report by Frisch and Meitner was not printed until March of that year, while the reports by American researchers, who had done their work later, were published before that date.

The process that came to be known as "fission" therefore read:

$$_{92}U \rightarrow {}_{56}Ba + {}_{36}Kr$$

Meitner and Frisch immediately made an estimate of the energy release that must accompany the fission process; they estimated it at about 200 million electron volts for every uranium atom that fissioned.

In our final report, reprinted as Appendix I of this book, we included, in addition to recounting our indicator experiments, the fact that thorium had also been split, though with fast neutrons instead of slow ones. We recognized the second portion of the debris of uranium fission as consisting of noble gases, the existence of krypton being proved by the presence of its decay products strontium and yttrium. The report included the indicator experiments with the alpha-radiating radium isotope thorium-X and the beta-radiating mesothorium, as well as the fractional crystallization of these with barium bromide. We found that barium chromate was even more effective in separating radium from barium. We explained how all this had been done with so few atoms that their existence could be detected only by the Geiger-Müller counter.

To cap it all, we designed a "circular process" with the long-lived barium-IV (originally called radium-IV). The purified preparation was separated into two unequal portions. The larger portion went through six chemically different barium salts, ending with barium chloride which had been the original material. After the decay products that had formed in the meantime had been removed, this material was compared with the smaller portion of barium chloride that had been saved for control purposes. Through all its compounds "barium-IV" had remained the same isotope—namely ordinary barium. This experiment might be labeled a "sixfold indicator experiment." Similar indicator experiments carried out with irradiated thorium proved that thorium will fission when subjected to bombardment with fast neutrons.

In discussing these experiments we stated that while the equation of the nuclear charges balanced properly, the mass number did not. On paper the mass numbers were always somewhat higher than those of the known barium and krypton isotopes, and we suspected that a few neutrons might have been set free in the process. We also tried, with absolutely inadequate equipment and therefore without success, to prove the existence of such free neutrons. Experimental proof was later furnished by many researchers. The first group to succeed was Dodé, von Halban, Joliot, and Kowarski (*Nature*, vol. 143, pp. 470 and 680,

1939). The knowledge that some neutrons are released when the uranium atom fissions brought the idea of utilizing the energy of the nuclei somewhat closer to realization.

Actually it is quite surprising how the chemical characteristics of an element, even of solitary atoms, can always be used for recognition. In the paper reprinted as Appendix I, we still said that "in our opinion" the transuranian elements maintained the positions assigned to them all along. These substances, which could be precipitated with hydrogen sulfide, did not seem to be directly connected with the noble gases and the alkali and alkaline earth metals which had been identified as fission products. But Lise Meitner and Frisch proved very quickly that two out of three atoms formed during fission had so much recoil that they could be found outside the uranium, even if they had to penetrate metal foil. They could have that much energy only because of fission; hence they could not be transuranian elements which had formed quietly by capturing a neutron. We as well as other researchers soon learned to recognize them as isotopes of tellurium, iodine, and molybdenum. Of the many transuranian elements the only one left was our "eka-rhenium," which its discoverers McMillan and Abelson named neptunium.

Recognition of the isotopes resulting from the fission of uranium and thorium then progressed rapidly. C. Lieber found not only several isotopes of barium but also three isotopes of strontium, showing that in addition to the split into barium and krypton there was one into strontium and xenon.

In a report finished in July 1939, Fritz Strassmann and I were able to give a great deal of additional information about isotopes of cesium, rubidium, xenon, krypton, iodine, and bromine. We could point out that the yield of fission products can differ in various respects—the iodine isotopes could be found very easily while the bromine isotopes had a far lesser intensity.

A member of the Institute's Physics Section, G. von Droste, investigated the energy distribution among the fission products and the mechanism of the production of free neutrons.

Going on the assumption that two or three free neutrons might result from each split uranium atom, S. Flügge of the Kaiser Wilhelm Institute for Chemistry published a carefully reasoned theoretical paper with the title: "Can the Energy Content of Atomic Nuclei Be Utilized in Technology?" (*Die Naturwissenschaften,* vol. 27, pp. 492–510, June 1939). Because of the free neutrons, he explained, the process of fission could be increased at will under certain conditions. One could visualize a chain reaction which would split every atom in a large lump of uranium. Flügge obtained the result that the fission of all uranium atoms in 1 cubic meter of U_3O_8 would release enough energy to lift 1 cubic kilometer of water (1000 million metric tons) to a height of 17 miles. Flügge also wondered how the rate of fission could be guided and if necessary reduced and suggested cadmium as a "neutron brake."

Flügge could not know at the time that the lump of uranium he assumed could not be consumed in a chain reaction without the presence of a moderator that reduced the velocity of the liberated neutrons. Certain other things had to be learned first, especially the fact that the main component (uranium-238) of the isotope mixture of natural uranium (U-235 + U-238) has nothing to do with the fission process; the responsible isotope is the rare uranium-235, which accounts for only 0.7 percent of the mixture. As is well known, the pursuit of this line of research led to the atom bomb, but since that research was not carried out at the Kaiser Wilhelm Institute, it does not belong in the framework of this book. There are, however, some interesting results of our own work which will now be discussed.

Disentangling the Radioactive Substances Produced by Fission

Proving the existence of short-lived fission products

In the last section of Chapter Six I explained a special version of the indicator method to which I gave the name emanation method. In this method the noble gases thoron and radon served not as chemical indicators for other gaseous isotopes but as indicators for the surface area and for changes in the surface area of substances in which such emanation is formed by the mother substance, either thorium-X or radium.

Since the fission of uranium and of thorium produces radioactive isotopes of the noble gases xenon and krypton, and since they in turn form isotopes of alkali and alkaline earth metals under emission of beta rays, it seemed logical to have the uranium or thorium at "maximum emanation" power during the neutron bombardment. This means that the noble gases should be able to diffuse from the preparation as much as possible. Previously the presence of the noble gases had been detected by blowing a strong jet of air over uranium or thorium during the neutron bombardment. This stream of air carried the gases along; the air was then led through chilled absorption coal, and the decay products, such as cesium and rubidium, were retrieved from the coal. But if the release of emanation is high the decay products of the emanation can be obtained directly. We utilized a method that had been current in radiochemistry for many years, especially in work with thorium—namely, concentrating the active deposit on a negatively charged electrode. The decay products from active noble gases can be dubbed "active deposits" as legitimately as the thorium-B and thorium-C deposits from emanating thorium.

Adapting our customary manner of experimentation to this problem meant keeping the following conditions in mind:

1. If the existence of very short-lived isotopes of xenon or krypton is to be ascertained, the irradiated uranium must really be in a state of maximum emanation to permit enough diffusion of the short-lived noble gases.
2. The negatively charged electrode collecting the "active deposit" must collect only the decay products of the noble gases; it must not collect any of the solid recoil particles.
3. The metal electrode must not be made radioactive by the neutrons used for irradiation.

The conditions were not hard to fulfill. Condition 1 was met by precipitating the ammonium uranate at a very low temperature and very fast, so that it formed a very fine powder with a very large surface. As for condition 2, only a very few of the recoil particles left the thick uranium layer; that those which did failed to reach the electrode for the "active deposit" could be shown by special experiments. Condition 3 was met by using cadmium which has an induced active isotope with a half-life of about 50 hours; hence an irradiation period of only a few minutes did not produce a noticeable quantity of this isotope. After longer irradiation periods the cadmium could easily be precipitated with hydrogen sulfide.

For our experiments with thorium we used a strongly emanating hydroxide made of our supply of thorium that had been steadily purified. The almost total absence of thoron-emitting radiothorium and thorium-X was pleasing since it made our work much easier.

Using this emanation method, we found two very short-lived alkali isotopes from uranium fission: one an active cesium with a half-life of about 40 seconds, the other an active rubidium with a half-life of 80 seconds.[2]

A brief description of our method might be of interest. By measuring the activated cadmium sheet immediately after short irradiation we found that it was possible to obtain measurable activities from very short-lived products after only 30 seconds, or even 15 seconds, of neutron bombardment.[3] A fraction of a minute was enough to produce noble gases from the uranium, to have them diffuse out of the thick ammonium uranate, and to make them deposit their decay products on the negatively charged cadmium electrode. Ten minutes after the termination of the neutron bombardment the quick decay was over and the further activities consisted of the formation of the alkali isotopes and *their* decay products. Analysis of the fairly complex curves permitted the conclusion that the 40-second and 80-second substance existed.

To find the chemical nature of these substances we had to make rapid separations. A method for the separation of cesium from rubidium was needed, and Fritz Strassmann found that silico-wolframic acid precipitated cesium, free from rubidium, with lightning speed. The filtering was done with membranes; then the precipitate was washed with a few drops of ether and measured. By practicing every movement we succeeded in making the measurements 1.2 to 1.4 minutes after the cessation of the neutron bombardment. As I reported then: "During this time the active substance had to be removed from the cad-

[2] *Author's Note. Nature* (vol. 143, pp. 516 and 679, 1939) carried a report by F. A. Heyn, A. H. W. Aten, Jr., and C. J. Bakker, about an unidentified alkali metal with a half-life of 1 or 2 minutes.

[3] *Author's Note.* In addition to the radium-beryllium tubes we were also able to use a high-voltage source for these experiments; it delivered about as many neutrons as would be produced by 6 to 7 grams of radium-beryllium.

mium electrode, precipitated, filtered, washed, covered with gummed cellophane, and measured in another room."

For most experiments the period of neutron bombardment was 1 minute. After analysis of the curves (keeping in mind the cesium, with a half-life of 7 minutes, and its decay products), we saw that they reflected half-lives of 39 to 41 seconds, a mean of 40 seconds—indubitably another cesium isotope. Therefore the 80-second substance had to be rubidium. The best and fastest means for precipitating rubidium was an alcoholic solution of chloride of tin with hydrochloric acid. But this precipitated the cesium along with the rubidium, and the activity of the cesium had to be subtracted from the total activity in order to find the half-life of the rubidium isotope. We succeeded in measuring the half-life in 1.6 to 1.8 minutes after terminating the irradiation and thus established a half-life of about 80 seconds for the rubidium isotope.

Details of this investigation were described in *Die Natur-wissenschaften* (vol. 28, pp. 54–61, 1940). The need for fast work when analyzing short-lived products became a kind of sporting activity. These experiments helped us greatly in working with other short-lived substances later.

Within one year after the discovery of uranium fission we had discovered sixteen fission products that were active isotopes of the elements krypton, rubidium, strontium, yttrium, xenon, cesium, barium, and lanthanum. We also established their half-lives. In addition, we found isotopes of noble gases with such short half-lives that their existence could only be inferred from their decay products.

Direct measurement of noble gases produced by fission

The use of uranium and thorium preparations with a large surface area, as described in the preceding section, certainly represented progress as compared to our earlier system which blew air through the preparation while the neutron bombardment was going on. Using the other method, we had been forced to draw our conclusions about the presence of the noble gases from their solid transformation products—cesium, rubidium, and others; in short, for the identification of noble gases the method was only an indirect one.

Then W. Seelmann-Eggebert built an apparatus at the Kaiser Wilhelm Institute for Chemistry by which the beta emission of active gases could be measured by means of a Geiger-Müller counter while they were still gases. Before that the presence of noble gases had been established directly by A. Langsdorf, Jr., and by E. Segrè and Miss C. S. Wu at the University of California at Berkeley. But these researchers had the Berkeley cyclotron with its high radiation output at their disposal and could make these measurements in ionization chambers. We could not do the same because our radiation sources were far weaker.

Seelmann-Eggebert investigated the primary gases from uranium fission and measured the half-lives of several gaseous isotopes which had been reported by others. A known cesium isotope with a half-life of 7 minutes was the product of a xenon isotope with a half-life of about 30 seconds which we obtained with a neutron bombardment of only 7 seconds—this short time was chosen to avoid producing longer-lived isotopes of the noble gases. Similarly a gaseous isotope with a half-life of 2.5 to 3 minutes was found; since it changed into rubidium it had to be a krypton isotope. Corroboration of the existence of this krypton isotope was furnished by work carried out independently by G. N. Glasow and J. Steigman.

The separation of krypton and xenon isotopes

Seelmann-Eggebert and others had established the existence of a krypton isotope with a half-life of 2.5 to 3 minutes, while Glasow and Steigman had described a rubidium isotope with a half-life of about 17 to 18 minutes. Since a rubidium isotope with a very similar half-life had been produced by a long-lived krypton isotope, it was of interest to verify the existence of these two obviously quite similar rubidium isotopes and to ascertain their half-lives with greater precision. In order to do this it was important to obtain a chemical separation of the rubidium isotopes to be investigated from the cesium isotopes present. The method we had used for proving the existence of the short-lived alkali-metal isotopes—separating the cesium as silico-wolframate—was not suited to this purpose. True, cesium that is free from rubidium is separated "in one blow," but quantitative conclusions cannot be drawn from the precipitate. On the other hand, rubidium that is precipitated from the filtrate in the form of rubidium stannic chloride always contains some cesium. The half-lives of the two short-lived alkali-metal isotopes could be determined, but the goal was to disentangle all the metallic isotopes resulting from the isotopes of the noble gases and for that a better separation of xenon from krypton was required.

We tried to find a direct method for the separation of the two noble gases and found it in the different rates of adsorption of xenon and krypton which resulted if the coal used for the adsorption had been chilled to different temperatures. We chilled the adsorption vessels first with a mixture of alcohol and solid carbon dioxide and then with liquid air. The charcoal was first boiled in hydrochloric acid to which 50 milligrams of cesium, 50 milligrams of rubidium, and smaller amounts of barium, strontium, lanthanum, and yttrium had been added. The alkali metals were precipitated with stannic chloride and the decrease of the activity of materials chilled to different temperatures measured. The decrease of activity in the coal chilled by carbon dioxide–alcohol proved to correspond to the decay of the cesium isotopes, while the coal chilled to lower temperatures with liquid air showed only the decay of rubidium isotopes.

By starting out with different durations of irradiation we were now able to disentangle the earlier confusion and to verify the previously uncertain findings about rubidium. There are indeed two different rubidium isotopes with very similar half-lives of 15.5 and 18 minutes, which originate from rather dissimilar krypton isotopes with half-lives of a few minutes and 3 hours, respectively. In any event, the adsorption of noble gases at different temperatures turned out to be a useful means of separating one from another.

About a nuclear isomer occuring during fission

The protactinium isotope uranium-Z which I had discovered was the first known case of a nuclear isomer. H. Götte was probably the first to prove the existence of an isomer among the fission products, which he did while investigating the xenon isotopes resulting from uranium fission. He used the Seelmann-Eggebert equipment for direct determination of the noble gases produced by fission. While investigating the xenon isotope with a half-life of 9 hours which, according to Langsdorf, Segrè, and Wu, is the product of an iodine isotope with a half-life of 6.6 hours, he also found a rapidly decaying substance, indicating a half-life of about 10 minutes.

That this short-lived gas, too, originated from the iodine isotope could be proved beyond doubt because the iodine was first separated from the irradiated uranium solution, and the two xenon isotopes were found in the iodine solution. By running systematic series of experiments, Götte could ascertain that the 10-minute xenon was formed by the 6.6-hour iodine, just as was the already-known 9-hour xenon. Unless one made the unlikely assumption that a second iodine isotope with practically the same half-life existed, he had a clear case of nuclear isomers. In a report (published in *Die Naturwissenschaften,* vol. 29, p. 496, 1941) Götte discussed the possibility of another probable case of isomers, this time two isotopes of yttrium produced by strontium.

Earlier in this chapter I described how we systematically tracked down and identified the various radioactive nuclei. It would lead us too far afield if I reported on, or reproduced, all our reports from the years 1939 to 1945. Still, it is interesting to show how the curves of decreasing radioactivity were analyzed and how, by varying the duration or the intensity of the neutron bombardment, we obtained, step by step, a gradual clarification of the situation. For this reason a report read to the Prussian Academy of Sciences in Berlin in 1942 is reprinted in this volume as Appendix II. At that time the work was still in progress and the report therefore contained only a part of the material we had already amassed, but it demonstrated our procedure. The report dealt especially with our work with the many strontium isotopes, their mother substances, and their decay products. Appendix III is a reprint of another report published by the Prussian Academy of Sciences, which concentrates on ways to separate the fission products chemically.

Although the report which is now Appendix III was published, it was not personally read to the Academy, because in March and April 1944 the Kaiser Wilhelm Institute for Chemistry was hit by bombs and damaged heavily. All work was interrupted, and as much of the equipment as possible was moved to the plants of manufacturers of synthetic fibers in Tailfingen in Württemberg. There we managed to continue some of the work and during the spring of 1945—near the end of the war—we were able to assemble a table showing all the products of uranium fission that we had found since 1939. The number we

Z/M	Se 34	Br 35	Kr 36	Rb 37	Sr 38	Y 39	Zr 40	Nb 41	Mo 42	– 43	Ru 44	Rh 45	Pd 46	Ag 47	Cd 48	In 49	Sn 50	Sb 51	Te 52	J 53	Xe 54	Cs 55	Ba 56	La 57	Ce 58	Pr 59	Nd 60	– 61	Sm 62	Eu 63	Z/M
83	14,0ᵐ	113ᵐ stab															stab														119
84		30ᵐ stab	stab														stab	-15ᵐ	stab												120
85		3ᵐ	46ʰ	stab													11ᵈ	stab													121
86			stab	18ᵐ	stab												stab	65ʰ	stab												122
87		50ᵐ	75ᵐ	610ᵐ	stab												80ʰ	stab	stab												123
88			175ᵐ	18ᵐ	stab												stab	60ᵈ	stab	-4ᵈ	stab										124
89			25ᵐ	15ᵐ	55ᵐ	stab											70ᵐ	?	stab												125
90			?	80½	5ᵃ	60ʰ	stab										20ᵐ	?	stab	13ᵈ	stab										126
91			?	?	10ʰ	50ᵈ 57ᵈ	stab										80ᵐ	90ᵐ 93ᵈ	stab												127
92			?	?	27ᵐ	35ᵐ	stab	11ᵐ	stab								stab	25ᵐ	stab												128
93						65ᵐ	55ᵈ stab										42ʰ	32ᵈ 72ᵐ	?	stab											129
94			?	?	2ᵐ	20ᵐ	stab	66ᵐ	stab								stab	25ᵐ	stab		stab										130
95						17ᵐ	75ᵐ	stab									12ᵈ 25ᵐ	8ᵈ	stab												131
96			?	?	7ᵐ	116ʰ	stab		stab		stab						5ᵐ	77ᵐ	24ʰ	stab		stab									132
97						26ᵈ	?	stab									10ᵐ	60ᵐ	20ʰ	5ᵈ	stab										133
98				6-10ᵐ	100½	?	?	stab	stab								43ᵐ	54ᵐ	stab	3ʰ	stab										134
99						67ᵐ	66ʰ langl	stab									66ᵐ	10ᵐ 95ᵐ	langl	stab											135
100					langl	stab	stab										18ᵐ	stab		stab		stab									136
101						146ᵐ	14ᵐ	stab									2ᵐ?	30ᵐ	38ᵐ	langl	stab										137
102						12ᵐ	kurzl	stab	210ᵐ	stab								17ᵐ	33ᵐ	stab		stab									138
103							20ʰ	50ʰ stab										45ᵐ	7ᵐ	87ᵐ	stab										139
104							-60ᵈ	?	stab	4,3ᵐ 44ᵐ	stab							?	40ᵐ	13ᵐ	40ᵐ	stab									140
105							-5ᵐ	-15ᵐ	4ʰ	34ᵐ	stab							?	?	6ᵐ	70ᵐ	15ᵈ	stab								141
106								1ᵃ	40ˣ	stab	-25ᵐ	stab						?	?	18ᵐ	35ᵐ	stab	187ᵐ	stab							142
107									15ʰ	40ᵐ stab										15ᵐ	40ᵐ	13ᵈ	stab								143
108									4ᵐ	25ᵐ	stab	24ᵐ	stab								310ᵈ	17ᵐ	stab	stab						144
109										31ᵐ stab											-4ʰ	100ᵈ	stab								145
110									stab	24ᵐ	stab										-15ᵐ	-25ᵐ	stab								146
111									26ᵐ	25ᵈ	stab											stab								stab	147
112									17ᵐ	32ʰ	stab	-64ᵐ	stab									stab									148
113									50ᵐ stab	104ᵐ stab													stab							stab	149
114									20ᵐ	stab	48ᵈ 72ᵐ	stab											stab		stab						150
115										56?	272ᵐ stab	stab														stab					151
116										-3ᵐ	stab	56ᵐ	stab												stab						152
117											170ᵐ	117ᵐ	stab													stab					153
118												stab															stab				154

Se Br Kr Rb Sr Y Zr Nb Mo – Ru Rh Pd Ag Cd Jn Sn Sb Te J Xe Cs Ba La Ce Pr Nd – Sm Eu

had established was about 100 radioactive isotopes of 25 different elements. Seelmann-Eggebert added a number of others which we had not actually found but which could be assumed to exist, for the most part mother substances of isotopes that we had found.

We of the Kaiser Wilhelm Institute for Chemistry had published all our findings, even during the war, but the first joint report of American, British, and Canadian researchers on fission products did not appear until November 1946,[4] more than a year and a half after the dropping of the atomic bombs. This report comprised a list of fission products, the chains of radioactive transformations, and a comprehensive list of references. There were 21 pages of tables listing elements, mass-numbers, half-lives, types of decay, isomers, and intensity of radiation. A total of 170 radiating fission products were listed, belonging to 36 different elements.

Of course our unpretentious table of early 1945 cannot be compared with this report in any way. Our weak neutron sources prevented us from finding either the substances that had long half-lives or those that appeared only in very small quantities. And at first only four scientists at the Kaiser Wilhelm Institute worked full time in this field—Strassmann, Seelmann-Eggebert, Götte and myself—later also H. J. Born and K. Starke. In contrast, the number of scientists employed by the Allies ran into hundreds. We have therefore no reason to feel ashamed of our more modest accomplishments.

Even during the last few days before the occupation we kept working. Born and Seelmann-Eggebert compared isotopes of the noble gases which were fission products with isotopes that are formed by their neighboring elements by neutron-alpha

[4] *Author's Note.* "Nuclei Formed in Fission: Fission Yields and Chain Relationships," *Journal of the American Chemical Society,* vol. 68, pp. 2411–2442, 1946.

and neutron-proton processes; Götte made similar comparisons with lanthanum isotopes. Born and Seelmann-Eggebert were also busy compiling a list of the maximal energies of the beta rays emitted by fission products.

What Substances Were
"Our" Transuranian Elements?

I listed two series of nuclear reactions and of radioactive isotopes which we had obtained by bombarding uranium with slow neutrons and which we thought to be transuranian elements. We had to assign that position to them because they seemed to originate from Fermi's two short-lived substances with 10-second and 40-second half-lives respectively. According to the knowledge of the time these two substances could only be artificial uranium isotopes. From them came the two series of elements that were named eka-rhenium, eka-osmium, eka-iridium, and eka-platinum, because they could be precipitated from acid solutions by means of hydrogen sulfide.

We now know that these two series were based on two fundamental errors. The main error was in accepting Fermi's short-lived substances as uranium isotopes; the second error was the assumption that these elements must have the chemical characteristics of the platinum metals, just because hydrogen sulfide would precipitate them from acid solutions. The true transuranian elements, found by Glenn T. Seaborg and his collaborators in the United States, are now known to have different chemical characteristics. These elements are often called "actinids," and it is now customary to consider thorium (no. 90), protactinium (no. 91), and uranium (no. 92), as "actinids," along with neptunium (no. 93), plutonium (no. 94), americium (no. 95), curium (no. 96), and so forth, up to the recently discovered no. 104. But the chemical characteristics of thorium, protactinium, and uranium can still be compared to those of their lower homologues, hafnium, tantalum, and wolfram.

Now that we know that our so-called transuranian elements were actually medium-heavy elements resulting from uranium fission, it is of interest to compare our findings with present knowledge.

Fermi's 10-second and 40-second substances were thought to represent uranium atoms that had captured one neutron; a chemical test of the 40-second substance which we had made with a view to establishing that it was uranium was published with many words of caution.

Checking our early results against Seaborg's comprehensive table of fission products, I found a krypton isotope with a half-life of 9.8 seconds, and a xenon isotope with a half-life of 16 seconds. These isotopes probably explain the old 10-second substance. Similarly, the 40-second substance could have been the krypton isotope with a half-life of 33 seconds or the xenon isotope with a half-life of 41 seconds.

The krypton and xenon isotopes change into alkali elements or alkaline earth elements, in some cases into isotopes of yttrium and of lanthanum. We did not find any of these because of the nature of the chemical separation we used. But among the fission products there are some elements—molybdenum and technetium on the one hand, and tin, antimony, and tellurium on the other—which would have responded in the same way as the platinum metals we thought we had, or, rather, as their higher homologues. It is difficult to assign definite places among the medium-heavy fission products for what we thought to be eka-rhenium, eka-osmium, eka-iridium, and eka-platinum. We did not have the means of determining their half-lives accurately enough to be certain that any one of them precisely corresponds to fission products determined by American researchers. Our eka-rhenium isotopes with half-lives of 2.2 minutes and 16 minutes might have been tin isotopes with similar half-lives, but isotopes of molybdenum and technetium cannot be ruled out.

Our eka-osmium isotopes with half-lives of 59 minutes and 5.7 hours were derived from eka-rhenium; hence, if we now consider our eka-rhenium to be tin, or molybdenum, or technetium, they were actually isotopes of antimony or technetium, or ruthenium. Our 5.7-hour eka-osmium might have been either the 4.6-hour or the 5.5-hour antimony isotope of Seaborg's table; but it could also have been the 4.5-hour ruthenium isotope. The 59-minute substance which we also considered eka-osmium is a puzzle. The chemical characteristics we found could fit an antimony isotope, but Seaborg's table does not contain an isotope with this or a similar half-life that has the proper chemical characteristics. I don't dare to say that our 59-minute substance has not been found by anybody else; our mixtures of various radioactive isotopes with different half-lives were often not very active and a mistake in establishing a half-life is therefore possible. But the 59-minute substance was obtained repeatedly.

It is certain that our eka-iridium and eka-platinum, with half-lives of 66 hours and 2.5 hours, were tellurium and iodine. The table of fission products we compiled in 1945 contains a tellurium isotope with a half-life of 3.2 days, or 77 hours, and an iodine isotope resulting from this tellurium isotope with a half-life of 2.4 hours. The precise modern values in Seaborg's table are 78 hours and 2.26 hours respectively.

In the case of eka-platinum we were again misled by our chemical tests. Of course we considered the substance to be eka-platinum because it formed directly from what we thought to be eka-iridium. When we precipitated the 2.5-hour substance with ammonium-platinum chloride it still seemed to resemble platinum, but in reality we did not obtain ammonium-eka-platinum chloride, as we had thought, but ammonium-platinum iodide, which is equally difficult to dissolve.

All our work was based on the assumption that uranium, when bombarded with neutrons, would react in the same manner as other elements; at the time there was no other explanation. The whole theoretical structure collapsed when it became known that atoms of uranium (and of thorium) will break apart; the short-lived uranium isotopes then turned out to be krypton and xenon isotopes, which undergo a number of transformations usually resulting in isotopes of medium-heavy metals.

Of course the American researchers did have a great advantage, in that we continued to publish the results of our work, even during the war, while they published nothing. Hence they were in a position to check on our research and to utilize it, but we couldn't learn anything from them. Considering this fact, we still have a certain amount of pride in our modest 1945 table which listed 100 different isotopes.

The Separation of Element No. 93, Neptunium

Some work accomplished by my collaborators, which was intimately connected with the separation of the fission products of uranium, must now be mentioned. As I have said, we had a beta-emitting substance, definitely a uranium isotope, with a half-life of 23 minutes (uranium-239). This had to produce the only true element, no. 93, but the final product did not greatly interest us, because we believed that we already had isotopes of element no. 93—our 2.2-minute and 16-minute eka-rhenium isotopes.

The direct separation of the true transuranian element no.

93 was complicated by the fact that it does not possess the characteristics expected of eka-rhenium. It seemed impracticable to obtain it indirectly via its mother substance uranium-239, the chemical characteristics of which were already known, since we knew that isotope 239 could not be chemically separated from the irradiated uranium-238, because they were isotopes of the same element. And since uranium-238 is naturally radio-active, it constantly forms decay products such as uranium-X_1 and X_2, which interfere with the recognition of the artificial isotope.

The actual transuranian element with a half-life of 2.3 days was, as has been mentioned, first found by McMillan and Abelson, who named it neptunium. Since they used a cyclotron, which is a very powerful radiation source, they could irradiate a very small amount of uranium, so that the natural decay products that were also found during the short time of irradiation did not noticeably interfere with the investigation of the substance into which the 23-minute isotope had changed. Our weak radiation sources forced us to irradiate larger quantities of uranium, and we observed what is now known as the Szilard-Chalmers effect. If you have a suitable uranium compound, the uranium nuclei that were not hit by a neutron will stay in the original compound, while all the nuclei that have been changed into the 23-minute isotope leave the molecules of which they had been a part and can therefore be separated chemically. In ordinary uranium compounds this kind of isotope separation will fail because an exchange of atoms is going on. But by irradiating a complex organic uranium compound, my collaborator K. Starke succeeded in enriching the compound with the 23-minute isotope by a factor of 100,000. Having accomplished this, he also succeeded in proving the existence of the decay product with a half-life of 2.3 days. (The experiments at my Institute were carried out independently, without knowledge of the American work, and had been practically completed when that work was published, but because of the war they could not be published until later.)

A very thorough investigation, the experimental part of which was chiefly carried out by Strassmann with improved measuring techniques and specially devised methods of chemical separation, culminated in the separation of neptunium that was pure as far as radioactivity was concerned. We then investigated the chemical characteristics, which at that time were quite mysterious. We did succeed in separating element no. 93 from uranium, uranium-X, and all the fission products. Starke, in 1943 and again in 1947, discussed the chemical nature of neptunium and its position in the Periodic Table.

Our attempts to find transuranian elements beyond neptunium were terminated by the events of 1945. It is now known that these elements form a sequence analogous to that of the rare earth elements and are not, as had long been thought, higher homologues of rhenium and the platinum metals.

Radiometric Adsorption Analysis

It was the Russian botanist Mikhail Semyonovitch Tswett who invented what has become known in English as "chromatography," and in German as "chromatographic adsorption analysis." The method is based on the fact that different organic substances are adsorbed in different places in an adsorption column. It was first used extensively in organic chemistry, and was later used by G. M. Schwab for separating inorganic ions. Then I suggested to my collaborator R. Lindner that a radiometric application should be possible—a column filled with aluminum oxide might be used to separate various types of radioactive atoms. The adsorbed atoms do not need to be treated further by chemical reactions, since the separation can be detected directly by measuring the activity in various places in the adsorbing column. Preliminary experiments with radioactive lead and bismuth showed that this method worked well. It was then used to separate radium from barium, which is a tedious operation with the "classical" method of fractional crystallization.

The next step was to try the method on the radium isotope thorium-X because its activity is easily measured. It was surprisingly successful; we obtained separations that were several hundred times as good as those obtained with the customary methods. In watery solutions the barium was found to be virtually free of radium. Equally good results were obtained with thorium-X and even with radium itself.

These gratifying results prompted Lindner to utilize adsorption analysis for the separation of rare earth elements. Many radioactive isotopes of rare earth elements were known, some of them fission products of uranium. Again the results were excellent; it was possible, for example, to separate praseodymium from lanthanum in a single operation. We were encouraged to try this method even with the ytterbium group of rare earths which are especially hard to separate from one another. The over-all outcome of these experiments was that radiometric adsorption analysis was found to be far superior to all earlier methods.

These experiments could not be continued after the end of the war, partly because of changes in personnel, partly because of the physical moves that became necessary. Nor was it necessary for us to continue them, since the idea of adsorption analysis had also occurred to American researchers. The reports of the work carried out during the years 1943–1947 appeared in the *Journal* of the American Chemical Society in 1947. As part of the Manhattan Project it had been done by several teams of researchers on a scale that would have been impossible in Germany.

The culmination of the American work was undoubtedly the isolation, in pure form, of element no. 61. This was accomplished by J. A. Marinsky, L. E. Glendenin, and C. D. Corryell, who called the element prometheum. It was obtained from isotopes that were fission products as well as from activated yttrium.

Now that the events that take place are better known, the purely descriptive name of "adsorption analysis" has been changed to "ion exchange."

The End of the War

On April 25, 1945, a small detachment of American and British soldiers, accompanied by a tank, appeared in Tailfingen, Württemberg. They inquired for the Kaiser Wilhelm Institute for Chemistry and having found it "invited" me to come along with them. The same thing happened at the Kaiser Wilhelm Institute for Physics, where a number of physicists, among them Max von Laue, were captured. The ranks were swelled by Werner Heisenberg, Carl Friedrich von Weizsäcker, and Walther Gerlach. Via France and Belgium we finally arrived at a beautiful country house near Cambridge, England. In France and Belgium we had been heavily guarded; but in England things were easier, and we were very well treated.

In 1945 the Nobel Prize Committee awarded me the prize in chemistry for the year 1944. Since I was not allowed to leave England at that time, the Prize was finally presented to me in Stockholm on December 10, 1946.

While I was still in England, Privy Councilor Max Planck, the Honorary President of the Kaiser Wilhelm Society, informed me that he and the directors of the Institutes had elected me their president. After some hesitation I accepted. Early in 1946 we were brought back to Germany, most of us to Göttingen, which was in the British Zone of Occupation; therefore I was President of the Kaiser Wilhelm Society in the British Zone. Professor Josef Mattauch took my old position, and Fritz Strassmann became head of the Department of Radiochemistry.

We gradually succeeded in convincing the Americans and the French that the Kaiser Wilhelm Society deserved recognition, but they refused to let us use its old name. In April 1948 it was reorganized as the Max Planck Society. I continued as president until May 1960 and then turned the presidency over to Professor Adolf Butenandt.

E I G H T

Epilogue

In looking back over my long life, I realize that my scientific career was due in large measure to a series of lucky accidents.

I owe it to the "father of my doctorate," Theodor Zincke, that after two years as his assistant, I was able to go to England and work with Sir William Ramsay—originally because I had to learn English for a promised job in the German chemical industry. Ramsay guided me into the realm of research on radioactivity, of which I knew nothing. There, by accident, I discovered the previously unknown radioactive element radiothorium.

Because of Ramsay's kindness I was able to establish personal ties with Emil Fischer of the Chemical Institute at the University of Berlin. Before going to Berlin, however, I traveled to Canada to work with Professor Ernest Rutherford, who was then the best source of information about radioactivity. And since the field was so new, it was not difficult to make discoveries. The three chains of radioactive decay were not yet well known and could be slowly established by the discovery of additional radioactive "elements" (actually isotopes).

Because the young physicist Lise Meitner joined me in Berlin in 1907, the chemical research work happily could be related to physics. In 1907 I attained professorial rank, but nowhere was there a chair for radiation research. To the physicists I was a chemist, to the chemists a physicist.

But then another lucky accident occurred: in 1911 the Kaiser Wilhelm Society was founded, and through Emil Fischer I was given the opportunity to form a small department for radoactivity research at the first Kaiser Wilhelm Institute, and Lise Meitner was soon allowed to join my department as a member of the scientific staff.

Then things started to expand. The "Department Hahn" became the "Department Hahn-Meitner," then split into "Department Hahn (Chemistry)" and "Department Meitner (Physics)." The Kaiser Wilhelm Institute for Chemistry became an Institute for Radiochemistry and Nuclear Physics.

During the year 1938, not long after Lise Meitner had been forced to leave Germany, Fritz Strassmann and I succeeded in interpreting the phenomena that had kept Hahn, Meitner, and Strassmann busy for four years. The classification of the countless artificial elements and nuclei was an especially interesting piece of work that lasted until the spring of 1945.

I don't think that I would have been capable of keeping in the forefront of research during the rapid developments that followed the end of the war. The new work involved entirely new means of research and a multitude of researchers. So it was a final lucky accident that I became president of the Kaiser Wilhelm Society in 1946 and instead of continuing research could contribute to the rehabilitation of that Society and the development of its successor, the Max Planck Society, during the fourteen years that followed.

Publisher's Postscript

Since the end of World War Two, Otto Hahn has lived in Göttingen. Deeply distressed by the first atomic explosions, for which he felt a personal responsibility, he has become a convinced opponent of atomic weaponry.

He shared the Enrico Fermi Award for 1966 with his colleagues, Professors Meitner and Strassman. The $50,000 award, made by the United States Atomic Energy Commission, is named in honor of the Italian physicist.

This was the first time that foreign scientists were named as recipients, and Professor Meitner was the first woman to be honored in this way.

Hahn and his associates were chosen to receive the Award jointly because of their combined and individual efforts in discovering nuclear fission and for their extensive experimental studies which led to this important discovery.

APPENDIXES

APPENDIX I

Proof of the Formation of Active Isotopes of
Barium from Uranium and Thorium Irradiated
with Neutrons; Proof of the Existence of More
Active fragments Produced by Uranium Fission.

BY OTTO HAHN AND FRITZ STRASSMANN, BERLIN-DAHLEM

(Originally published in *Die Naturwissenschaften*, 1939, vol.
27, no. 6, under the title: *"Nachweis der Entstehung activer
Bariumisotope aus Uran und Thorium durch Neutronenbestrahlung; Nachweis weiterer aktiver Bruchtücke bei der Uranspaltung."* An editorial note stated that the manuscript was
received January 28, 1939.)

A. Final Proof of the Origin of
Barium from Uranium

In a report which appeared recently in this journal,[1] we
stated that the new radioactive substances produced by irradiating uranium with neutrons, which originally had been
thought to be isotopes of radium, have the chemical characteristics of barium and are evidently not radium but isotopes of

[1] *Die Naturwissenschaften*, vol. 27, p. 11, 1939.

barium.[2] In the following we wish to prove this assertion and to extend it also to thorium. In the scheme of radioactive decay in our last report we listed four "radium" isotopes, of which three had been proved to exist and half-lives had been established for them. The fourth "radium" isotope, labeled Ra-I, was assumed to have a very short half-life, and its existence had been deducted from another substance which was taken to be its decay product.

As regards the three alkaline earth metals the existence of which had been proved, they could be only radium or barium; strontium and calcium had been eliminated. Since fractionating crystallization with barium salts did not produce the results to be expected from radium, we made a number of indicator experiments with radium isotopes known to be such, so that we could ascertain the chemical behavior of the alkaline earth metals produced by uranium.

The indicator experiments are described and numerically evaluated in the following. They were carried out on the one hand, with "radium-III" with a half-life of 86 minutes and "radium-IV" with a half-life of 300 hours, and on the other with the long-known radium isotopes mesothorium-1 (a beta-ray emitter) and thorium-X (an alpha-ray emitter). From now on we shall use Ba-III and Ba-IV instead of Ra-III and Ra-IV.

The following combinations were investigated:

1. Ba-III + Mesothorium-1, fractionated with barium bromide.
2. Ba-III + Thorium-X, fractionated with barium chromate.
3. Ba-IV + Thorium-X, fractionated with barium chromate.
4. A "circular process" with a series of crystallizing barium salts was carried out.

In experiment 1 a quantity of about 15 grams of purified uranium was irradiated for 12 hours with radium-beryllium neutrons. After stopping the irradiation we waited for 2½ hours so that the Ba-II with its short half-life of 14 minutes could decay. Thus we obtained mainly the 86-minute isotope Ba-III with a small quantity of the 300-hour Ba-IV. Then 2 grams of

[2] *Ibid.*, vol. 26, p. 755, 1938.

barium in the form of its chloride were precipitated from the solution containing the irradiated uranium and afterwards the barium in the form of its carbonate. A radium-free mesothorium preparation of known intensity had its decay products removed and was then also precipitated as its carbonate. The two carbonates were dissolved together in bromic acid and the bromides then crystallized in the manner that is used for obtaining radium. During this fractionating crystallization the decay products of the active barium isotopes were steadily removed, as was the mesothorium-2 produced by mesothorium-1, so that we had pure barium and radium salts. During the decay of the Ba-III (86-minute half-life) the figures for the activity of this substance have to be calculated for a common zero time (the beginning of the first crystallization); the formation of mesothorium-2 from the constantly active mesothorium-1 has to be calculated for each crystallization. Figure I-1 shows the results for 500 milligrams (each) of anhydrous barium bromide. Curves I, II, and III in the left-hand section of the diagram show the intensities as measured for a period of more than 70 hours, up to the radiation balance between mesothorium-1 and mesothorium-2. The ratio of the mesothorium content of the fractions I, II, and III is 67.6, 25, and 11; six times as much in the first fraction than in the third.

The center section of the diagram shows the beginnings of the activity curves for the first 500 minutes on a larger scale. The three broken lines show the increase of activity due to mesothorium-2. The right-hand section of the diagram shows the decrease of Ba-III by the differences between curves I, II, and III and the mesothorium curves.

The inclination of the lines in the right-hand section corresponds to the 86-day half-life of Ba-III. The line representing the second fraction is a little lower than the lines for the first and the third fractions, but the difference is certainly within the limits of experimental error. The Ba-III lines show a very faint flattening because the 12-hour irradiation of the uranium also produced some Ba-IV which has a 300-hour half-life. If the curves are calculated for zero time, we find the values of 81, 72,

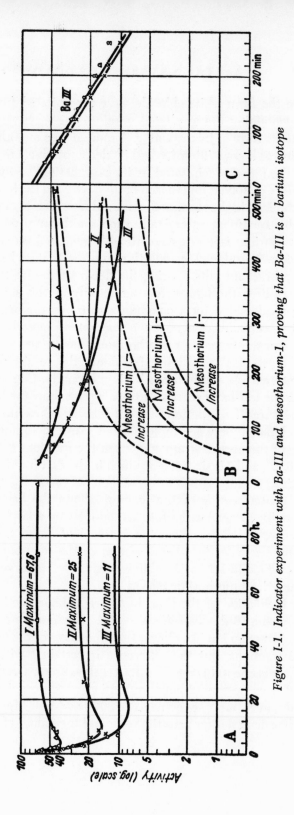

Figure I-1. Indicator experiment with Ba-III and mesothorium-1, proving that Ba-III is a barium isotope

and 81 for the activities of the three fractions; a difference of about 10 percent.

Comparing the results with the 6:1 "enrichment" of the radium isotope mesothorium-2, we see that there has been no "enrichment" for the Ba-III; proof that it differs from radium and a strong hint of its identity with barium.

In experiment 2 11 grams of purified uranium were irradiated with neutrons for 3 hours. After waiting for 2½ hours to permit the Ba-II to decay, 1 gram of barium was added in the form of barium chloride which was then precipitated with 37-percent hydrochloric acid, then dissolved and reprecipitated. The pure barium chloride was then added to a solution of the radium isotope thorium-X from which all decay products had been removed and then the active barium and the thorium-X were precipitated together as barium carbonate. This was then dissolved in weak nitric acid, enough ammonium chromate for a reaction with the larger part of the barium was added, and the precipitation was started by adding ammonium acetate drop by drop. The thorium-X had been separated from a pure radiothorium preparation with the help of ammonia and had been precipitated with the barium as barium carbonate. When the radiothorium is precipitated with ferric acid, the thorium-B and thorium-C go into the precipitate and the thorium-X is perfectly pure. After most of the barium had been precipitated as its chromate, the solution was filtered and then the remainder of the barium was precipitated with more ammonium chromate and ammonium acetate. Of the first main fraction, two samples of $BaCrO_4$, weighing 500 and 380 milligrams, respectively, were measured. Of the smaller second fraction only one 350 milligram sample was measured.

Figure I-2 shows the results. The left-hand portion of the diagram again shows the direct values of the intensities; the decrease in the beginning is caused by the decay of the 86-minute isotope, the intensity of which at the beginning is to be determined. The maximum activities of the two curves I*a* and I*b* are not quite proportional to their weights of 380 and 500 milligrams. The layer of the precipitate from the 380-milligram

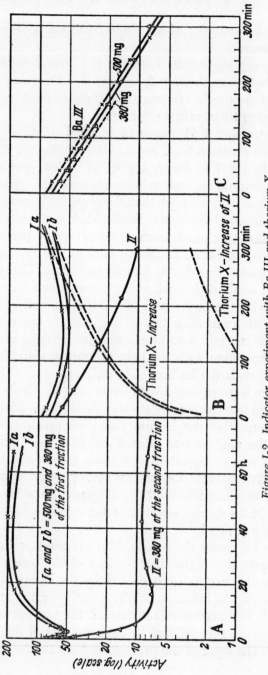

Figure I-2. Indicator experiment with Ba-III and thorium-X

sample is thinner and permits a larger percentage of the soft beta rays from thorium-B to enter the counter. It is therefore necessary to compare equal weights—namely fraction I*b* and fraction II. The maximum activities are about 175 and a little below 9. The enrichment of the radium isotope thorium-X in the first fraction, compared with the second fraction, showed the ratio of 19:1. The experiment had turned out very well indeed.

The center section of Figure I-2 again shows the beginning of the curves indicating the decrease of the 86-minute Ba-III and the increase of thorium-X. The broken-line curves by themselves show the thorium-X increases. If these are subtracted from the total activity, we obtain the activity of the 86-minute Ba-III alone (see the right-hand section of the diagram). The three lines are close together and their absolute activity at zero time was identical. Because of the shorter irradiation time no Ba-IV was formed, so that no flattening appears in these lines. The top line is that of the 500-milligram sample; calculating for 380 milligrams, we obtain the bottom broken line, showing that the thicker layer absorbed a little more of the beta rays. While the radium isotope thorium-X showed an enrichment of 19.5:1, there was no change in the activities of the Ba-III in the fractions: *proving that it is different from radium and identical with barium.*

In experiment 3 the long-lived Ba-IV and the radium isotope thorium-X were used, both of these being substances which, when free of their decay products, show an initial increase in activity which is then followed by a decrease proportional to their half-lives of 300 hours and 3.64 days. The Ba-IV was obtained by irradiating 5.4 grams of uranium for one month. After waiting for one day so that the Ba-II and Ba-III could decay, the Ba-IV was precipitated from the solution with barium chloride, the precipitate dissolved, and then the barium precipitated as a carbonate. The thorium-X was separated from the radiothorium in the manner previously described. The two carbonate precipitates containing the Ba-IV and the thorium-X and weighing 2–3 grams were dissolved together in hydrochloric acid, precipitated once more as barium chloride, and dissolved in weak nitric acid. What followed was similar to experiment 2 in that the barium underwent fractionated precipitation as its chromate. The following fractions were obtained:

Fraction I = 200 milligrams of chromate
Fraction II = 500 milligrams of chromate
Fraction III = ca. 1 gram of chromate
Fraction IV = 500 milligrams of chromate

Of these fractions I, II, and IV were measured.

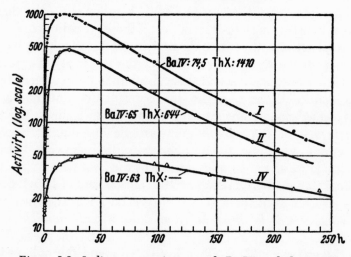

Figure I-3. Indicator experiment with Ba-IV and thorium-X

We first observed the formation of the active deposit from thorium-X and the decay products of the long-lived Ba-IV. Thorium-X reached its maximum after about 40 hours, and Ba-IV after about 100 hours. After a month thorium-X has decayed completely, but about 20 percent of the Ba-IV and its decay products are left, and one can then obtain directly the distribution of the Ba-IV in the several fractions. But Figure I-3 shows that we didn't have to wait that long. Curve I shows the activity of the first fraction (200 milligrams). The values observed were multiplied by 2.5 so that they would apply to the weight of fractions II and IV (500 milligrams each). After the maximum had been passed, the activity in each curve was compounded of the decay rates of thorium-X and Ba-IV. It is not difficult to calculate the activity of the two components. The results are:

	Ba-IV (units)	Thorium-X (units)
Fraction I	74.5	1410
Fraction II	65	644
Fraction IV	63	almost zero

As has been stated, in the case of fraction I only 200 milligrams were measured and the value recalculated for 500 milligrams, but the thinner layer permitted the measuring of higher radiation; hence the value of 74.5 for fraction I must be too large. *Considering this fact we have in each of the measured three fractions the same activity for the barium and very different activities for the thorium-X.* Because of the very large fraction III which was not measured, fraction IV contains practically no thorium-X any more. *The result is again the same as before: Ba-IV is barium and certainly not radium.*

It may be mentioned in passing that a well-handled fractionation of a radium-barium mixture in the form of chromates enables one to obtain pure radium much faster than the still-customary fractionation of the bromides or especially of the chlorides.

Experiment 4, which was the last of the experiments to prove the chemical identity of the active Ba-IV with normal inactive barium, was a "circular process" that may be described briefly. The active barium isotopes, after an addition of 2.5 grams of barium chloride, were separated from the irradiated uranium in the customary manner, reprecipitated after the decay of Ba-II and Ba-III, and three-fourths of the quantity sent through the following set of barium precipitations: (1) barium chloride $\longrightarrow$ (2) barium succinate $\longrightarrow$ (3) barium nitrate $\longrightarrow$ (4) barium carbonate $\longrightarrow$ (5) barium chloride $\longrightarrow$ (6) barium ferrimannite [3] $\longrightarrow$ (7) barium chloride.

[3] We wish to express our thanks to Professor Wilhelm Traube for calling our attention to this interesting complex organic barium compound which he synthesized for the first time.

After our barium had gone through all these compounds it was crystallized once more for final purification, and the one-fourth of the original material that had been kept as a control preparation was recrystallized at the same time. Then two samples of the "circular barium" and two samples of the control preparation (each sample weighing 250 milligrams) were measured with the same counter. As Figure I-4 shows, all samples

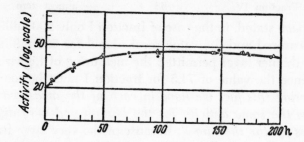

Figure I-4. The "circular experiment" with Ba-IV. The small circles indicate the readings of sample No. 1 of the "circular" barium; the crosses those of sample No. 2; the triangles and dots show the readings of the control samples

read the same, discounting the unavoidable small deviations. *Throughout all these crystallizations the Ba-IV stayed with its inactive isotope barium.*

B. Proof That the Irradiation of Thorium with Neutrons also Yields Barium Isotopes

After it had been proved experimentally that the fission of uranium yields several isotopes of barium, it was an obvious move to check whether the "radium isotopes" from thorium which Lise Meitner and the co-authors of this report had announced [4] actually were radium or also barium. The experiments are somewhat more difficult with thorium because the available

[4] Meitner, Strassmann, and Hahn, in *Zeitschrift für Physik*, vol. 109, p. 538, 1938.

intensities are quite small but the results leave no doubt that the isotopes formed are also isotopes of barium and not of radium. Both the "15-minute radium" and the 4-hour radium" from thorium were checked; thorium-X was used as an indicator for both, and the fractional crystallization was carried out with their chromates.

Figure I-5 shows the results of the "15-minute radium" from thorium; the left-hand portion of the diagram again shows the activity curves for 500 milligrams of chromate. The actual measurements are quite scattered, which is not surprising since the activity at the beginning amounted to 15–20 particles per minute. The maximum value for thorium-X in the first fraction is 103, in the second fraction 17.5. The center section of the diagram shows the measurements during the first 200 minutes; the broken lines indicate the formation of the active deposit from thorium-X. The right-hand portion of the diagram shows the measured activities after subtracting the contribution from thorium-X. We obtained two curves of roughly the same intensity; they show the decay of the 15-minute substance and its product lanthanum. If the activity of the lanthanum, which has a half-life of about 3½ hours, is subtracted from these curves, we obtain the two straight lines at the bottom which show half-lives of 20 and 21 minutes instead of the correct value of 15 minutes. Even though the results are less beautiful than in the case of uranium, one can see that the initial activities of the alkaline-earth metals are practically the same, whereas thorium-X displays a ratio of 6 : 1. The 15-minute substance that is formed by irradiating thorium with fast neutrons is certainly not radium. Since its general chemical characteristics leave only a choice between radium and barium—it cannot possibly be strontium—one is justified in concluding that it is barium.

Analogous experiments with the 4-hour substance formed by thorium with thorium-X as the indicator have been carried out. Since the results were not very good because of the weak initial activity, we refrain from printing the diagram. The somewhat uncertain calculated results were that the activities in the three fractions of the 4-hour substance were about 1½ : 1 : 1½,

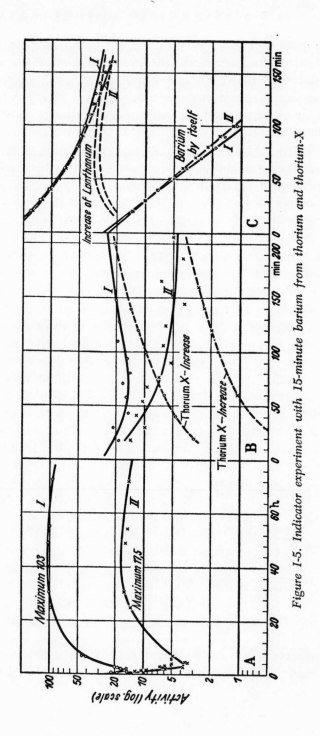

Figure I-5. Indicator experiment with 15-minute barium from thorium and thorium-X

and for thorium-X they were 20 : 5 : 1. We therefore believe that the 4-hour substance from thorium is identical with barium.

These results make it understandable why Dr. von Droste [5] of our Institute, in spite of careful work and great diligence, failed to find the alpha particles, believed necessary for the formation of radium from thorium, after the irradiation of thorium with fast neutrons. While the uranium atom will fission under the influence of slow neutrons, neutrons of considerable energies are needed to fission the thorium nucleus.[6]

Whether the nuclei of stable inactive elements like bismuth and lead can be made to fission could be learned only by experiments with still more energetic neutrons. It certainly will be advisable to check very carefully the chemical characteristics of any active isotopes obtained in future experiments and not to restrict the investigation to the immediate neighbors of the irradiated substances.

C. A Few Questions Concerning These New Results; Proof of Additional Fragments of Uranium Nuclei

The proof that alkaline-earth metals produced by the fission of uranium and of thorium are barium isotopes raises a large number of new questions of which the following may be mentioned:

1. Is it possible to make a statement about the atomic weights of the artificial barium isotopes?
2. Are the barium isotopes from thorium the same as those from uranium?
3. Are the decay products of the barium isotopes definitely lanthanum and cerium isotopes?
4. Will the "transuranian elements" maintain their positions?
5. What are the other fragments that are formed by the fission of uranium and thorium nuclei?

[5] G. von Droste in *Zeitschrift für Physik,* vol. 110, p. 84, 1938.
[6] Meitner, Hahn, and Strassman, *op. cit.*

It goes without saying that not all of these questions can be answered at this time; but a few things can be stated.

As regards the first question, we determined that the half-life of Ba-III from uranium is 86 minutes. Irradiating inactive barium with neutrons yielded a beta-ray-emitting radiobarium with a half-life of 85 minutes, its probable atomic weight being 139.[7] We confirmed the existence of such an active barium isotope with such a half-life. Even after an irradiation lasting 6 days no hint of an active decay product from this radiobarium could be found. If the atomic weight of radiobarium is actually 139, no active decay product is to be expected, since lanthanum with the same atomic weight is a stable isotope. If our Ba-III is identical with this radiobarium—the figures for the half-lives are in favor of this assumption—then our carefully advanced claim for a lanthanum isotope with a half-life of several days as a decay product of Ba-III must be a mistake. We must have been deceived by the unavoidable presence of Ba-IV and its decay products that are known to exist. We now think it quite probable that Ba-III actually is identical with radiobarium and therefore has an atomic weight of 139. A few recent experiments favor this assumption.

As regards the other barium isotopes from uranium fission, one might hypothesize that barium-IV is the mother substance of a radiolanthanum with a half-life of 31–46 hours and an atomic weight of 140, which has been described in the literature (see Diebner and Grassmann, *op. cit.*). The lanthanum isotope we found to form in Ba-TV has a half-life of about 36 hours. If this is the case, one might try to derive Ba-IV from ordinary barium by long-lasting irradiation from powerful neutron sources and check on its decay into an active lanthanum isotope.

We cannot say anything about the atomic weights of the short-lived barium isotopes, of which Ba-I is still hypothetical. But to avoid misunderstanding, we wish to emphasize once more than the isotopes we called Ba-II, Ba-III, and Ba-IV are barium isotopes and that none of them can be strontium.

[7] See Diebner and Grassmann, *Künstliche Radioaktivität* (Leipzig: S. Hirzel, 1939).

As for question 2: the half-lives of the isotopes which Lise Meitner and the authors originally dubbed radium isotopes (now known to be barium isotopes) and their decay products that began with thorium are compared with those of the barium isotopes and their decay products that began with uranium, the similarity of the two groups is conspicuous.

The schemes are:

For the substances from uranium:

$$\text{Ba-I} - \beta - \text{La-I} -$$
$$<1 \text{ min.} \qquad <30 \text{ min.}$$

For the substances from thorium:

$$\text{Ba(Th)} - \beta - \text{La(Th)} -$$
$$<1 \text{ min.} \qquad 18 \text{ min.}$$

In the third group the similarities are weak; Ba-III has a half-life of 86 minutes; for the third barium from thorium a half-life of 3½–4 hours was found. In spite of the low radiation intensities with which we had to work, we find it difficult to assume that the half-life for the third barium from thorium could be wrong to such an extent.

It would be interesting, and, with strong neutron sources and long irradiation time, easily possible to find a long-lived barium isotope from thorium comparable to the Ba-IV from uranium. Irradiations lasting several hours a day, repeated for a period of several days, should produce long-lived substances from a thorium that does not contain much radiothorium. During this period there would be much activity from the radium isotopes thorium-X and mesothorium-1, but these two radium isotopes could be removed by a series of barium-chromate fractionations. The characteristic behavior of Ba-IV should then be easily recognizable.

As for question 3, namely whether the decay products of the barium isotopes from uranium and from thorium are definitely lanthanum and cerium, this has not yet been investigated in detail. But we previously reported that the active product from Ba-II (then called Ra-II) is certainly not actinium and shows the general characteristics to be expected of lanthanum. This is a field in which systematic experiments will have to be made.

Question 4 touched a most important point, namely the position of the "transuranian" elements investigated by the authors in collaboration with Lise Meitner. Do these elements remain in the positions assigned to them, or are they elements with much lower atomic numbers? In our last report [see footnote 1] we hinted that the atomic weights of a barium isotope and a masurium isotope, say 138 + 101, would result in an uranium isotope of the weight 239. Instead of considering the elements from eka-rhenium to eka-platinum as transuranian elements, one could consider those from masurium to palladium. From a few experiments which we have made, and in view of the general chemical characteristics of the transuranian elements eka-osmium to eka-platinum on the one hand and those of the lower homologues of platinum on the other hand, it seems to us impossible that the transuranian elements are actually the lower platinum homologues. The direct investigation of eka-platinum for its possible identity with palladium produced a negative result. Even a slight shift of the substances to higher or lower atomic numbers, say to molybdenum in the one direction and to silver in the other, does not seem likely. As far as silver is concerned, it was proved by specific experiments that none of the transuranian elements is silver.

One could still consider the series gallium, germanium, arsenic, and selenium. But of these, arsenic, selenium, and germanium must be ruled out, because of their general chemical characteristics as well as because of experiments made for the purpose.

We have therefore returned to the opinion that these *are* transuranian elements. We may have to make an exception in the case of the 60-day substance discovered by Hahn, Meitner, and Strassmann.[8] We had not assigned a definite place to this substance but had thought that it might be an isomer of eka-iridium. This will require a special investigation, because now,

[8] *Die Naturwissenschaften*, vol. 26, p. 475, 1938.

after it has been shown that the uranium nucleus will fission, the 60-day substance could be something entirely different.

As for question 5, if the transuranian elements cannot be considered fragments of an uranium nucleus as the barium isotopes are, we have to ask ourselves what they might be.

Since a splitting by units of atomic weight—for example, the formation of masurium and other neighboring elements—evidently does not take place, one might consider splitting by units of atomic number which would lead to the emission of a number of neutrons. If the uranium nucleus with its 92 units of charge forms barium with its 56 charge units, an element with a nuclear charge of 36 units would be left over—that is to say, krypton. This could then turn into rubidium, strontium, and yttrium, and possibly others. *Of these active elements that were to be expected, the strontium could be easily isolated.* A solution of irradiated uranium received an addition of 150 milligrams of strontium. This solution was freed of the transuranian elements present by precipitating them with hydrogen sulfide and then a precipitation with ammonia was carried out. The uranium precipitate was dissolved in nitric acid (65 percent), and with the aid of fuming nitric acid, strontium nitrate was precipitated. The strontium nitrate was then dissolved in water, 60–70 milligrams of barium were added, and in a weak solution of acetic acid the strontium nitrate was separated with ammonium chromate. This separation is necessary because strontium nitrate will form a coprecipitate with the barium that is produced by the irradiation. The strontium was then precipitated in the form of strontium carbonate from the filtrate of the barium chromate. It was then dissolved in hydrochloric acid, 10 milligrams of yttrium were added to the solution, and the yttrium was precipitated with ammonia that was free of any carbonates. Finally the strontium was precipitated as its carbonate from the filtrate and measured. This series of separations removes the transuranian elements—uranium, uranium-X, and uranium-Z; also barium and its decay products: lanthanum and cerium; and yttrium, zirconium, and others that may have been produced by the strontium. It also removes calcium, if present. The resulting active strontium, from 4 grams of uranium that had been irradiated for several days, always produced several hundred units of radiation, the decrease of which could be followed for several days. *This proved that strontium had been formed.*

The beta-radiating strontium must produce yttrium, and yttrium that has been formed by strontium decay is easy to separate. This is done by a precipitation with ammonium free of carbonates and by a reprecipitation in the presence of inactive strontium. The yttrium precipitates that were produced in this manner had easily measurable activities that could also be followed for several days. Therefore the formation of yttrium can be considered proved.

Finally we found a simple method for proving the formation of noble gases and of alkali metals. A concentrated solution of 50 grams of uranyl-nitrate in water was irradiated for 2–5 hours. During this period a stream of air of varying velocities was blown through the solution and it then passed through a cotton filter 20 centimeters in length; the air then entered an absorption container filled with water of very slight acidity. After the irradiation was stopped, the contents of the absorption vessel received 50 milligrams of cesium chloride (rubidium could not be used because of its natural beta-ray activity), and then the cesium was precipitated in the form of cesium-platinum chloride. Its activity was then measured. After that, some strontium was added to the filtrate of the cesium-platinum chloride, and a carbonate precipitation was made. Both the cesium and strontium precipitates showed measurable activities. In both cases the active substances had rather short half-lives. The same series of experiments without irradiation of the uranium produced substances that were completely inactive. Evidently these decay processes also were mixtures of isotopes, but we cannot say anything yet about their number or their half-lives.

In addition to this direct proof for the formation of an alkali and an alkaline earth metal, the experiment also proved the formation of one of the noble gases. Whether it was krypton, producing rubidium and strontium, or xenon, producing cesium and barium, could not yet be ascertained. Later investigations are

204

expected to show whether the uranium nucleus produces barium and krypton as the primary fission products, or whether these are strontium and xenon.

During the writing of the reports on our latest experiments we received the manuscripts of two articles which are to appear in *Nature,* one by Lise Meitner and O. R. Frisch, the other by O. R. Frisch. We wish to thank the authors for sending them to us. Meitner and Frisch discuss in their manuscript the possibility of the fission of uranium and thorium nuclei into two fragments of about equal mass, for example, barium and krypton. They discuss the possibility of such an event with regard to Niels Bohr's latest atomic model. O. R. Frisch reports on experimental proof of the formation of energetic fragments of the nuclei of uranium and thorium after neutron irradiation.

In concluding, we wish to thank Miss C. Lieber and Miss I. Bohne for their assistance with our many experiments.

Summary

1. The formation of barium isotopes from uranium was proved.
2. The formation of barium isotopes from thorium was also proved.
3. Some information about the atomic weights of some of the new barium isotopes could be given.
4. Apparently the barium isotopes from thorium are identical with the barium isotopes from uranium.
5. In our opinion the "transuranian elements" remain in their position.
6. As a secondary group of fragments, strontium and yttrium were found.
7. By a proper experimental arrangement the formation of a noble gas was proved, which, in turn, produces an alkali metal. The decision as to whether this is xenon to cesium or krypton to rubidium could not yet be made. In one case the decay products would be barium and lanthanum, in the other strontium and yttrium, all of which have been found.

That the many new decay products that have been described could be found so quickly and—as we believe—with great certainty was made possible by the experience which we, in collaboration with Lise Meitner, had acquired during our systematic experiments about transuranian elements and the decay products of thorium.

APPENDIX II

*Remarks on the Experimental Disentanglement
of the Elements and Isotopes Produced by the
Fission of Uranium.*

BASED ON EXPERIMENTS CARRIED OUT BY OTTO HAHN, FRITZ STRASS-
MANN, AND HANS GÖTTE. READ AT THE MEETING OF THE SECTION OF
MATHEMATICS AND NATURAL SCIENCE OF THE PRUSSIAN ACADEMY
OF SCIENCES, ON DECEMBER 4, 1941.

(Originally published in the *Abhandlungen der Preussischen
Akademie der Wissenschaften* (Jahrgang 1942, Mathematisch-
naturwissenschaftliche. Klasse No. 3) under the title of:
*"Einiges über die experimentelle Entwirrung der bei der Spal-
tung des Urans auftretenden Elemente und Atomarten."*)

The fission of the uranium atom, which was discovered
early in 1939 by Hahn and Strassmann, results in a series of
elements of medium weight which usually appear in the form
of several isotopes. In less than three years their number has
grown so large that no one not conversant with the details of the
experimental technique can quite understand in what manner
these substances could be disentangled. So far twenty-three elements have been found to be represented, and because they

TABLE I A

Fragments resulting from the fission of uranium-235, known in 1941

Mass:	34 Se	35 Br	36 Kr	37 Rb	38 Sr	39 Y	40 Zr	41 Nb	42 Mo	43 Tc	44 Rb
>82		50ˢ→									
>82		3ᵐ→									
>82		30ᵐ→									
83	ca 30ᵐ→	140ᵐ→	113ᵐ ↓ stable								
88		175ᵐ→	17.8ᵐ→	stable							
89		2.5ᵐ→	15.4ᵐ→	55ᵈ→	stable						
90					2ᵈ→	60.5ʰ→	stable				
(91)			very short→	80ˢ→	2.7ᵐ→	3.5ʰ→	stable				
>91				? →	? →	8.5ʰ	↗ 57ᵈ ↘ 50ᵐ	stable			
>91				? →	? →	7ᵐ→	9ʰ→	?			
>91						ca 20ᵐ→	?				
93							65ᵈ→				
95							17ʰ→	75ᵐ→	stable		
?								26ᵈ ?			
99									67ʰ→	6.6ʰ +long-lived	
101									14.6ᵐ→	14ᵐ→	stable
>101									12ᵐ→	very short	

Mass:	51 Sb	52 Te	53 I	54 Xe	55 Cs	56 Ba	57 La	58 Ce	59 Pr
127	$80^h \to$	90^d							
		↓							
		$9.3^h \to$	stable						
129	$4.2^h \to$	32^d							
		↓							
			$72^m \to$	?					
131		1.2^d							
		↓							
			$25^m \to$	$8^d \to$	stable				
>131	$5^m \to$	$77^h \to$	$2.4^h \to$	?					
133	$10^m \to$	$60^m \to$	$185^h \to$	4.3^d					
>131		$43^m \to$	$54^m \to$	?					
135	$15^m \to$	$6.6^h \to$	9.5^h ↗ / 10^m ↘						
>131			$30^s \to$	?					
>131		$1.8^m \to$	?						
>136			$17^m \to$	$32^m \to$	?				
139				$45^s \to$	$7^m \to$	$86^m \to$	stable		
139				$45^s \to$	$7^m \to$	$86^m \to$	stable		
140				very short	$40^s \to$	$300^h \to$	$44^h \to$	stable	
141/143			? $\to$	? $\to$	ca $6^m \to$	ca $70^m \to$	ca $15^d \to$	?	
>142			? $\to$	? $\to$	ca $18^m \to$	ca $3.5^h \to$	ca $300^d \to$	?	
>140							ca $15^m \to$	?	

simultaneously form several isotopes, the total number of isotopes is slightly larger than eighty.

The problems that have to be solved in this case are far more complicated than those of the better-known nuclear transformations, where it is only necessary to prove the existence of or to obtain a separation of atoms with the same atomic number or their immediate neighbors in the atomic table. The chemist's job is to find the fission products, to establish their proper place in the Periodic Table, and to explain the series of transformations from the primary fission products to inactive isotopes. But we are still far away from a certain identification of the *primary* fission products and it is certain that many of the intermediary products, especially those with short half-lives, are still unknown. Tables I A and I B show the isotopes that have been found so far.[1]

In general, and this has to be emphasized, the work with artificial isotopes always involves proving the presence of quantities that are invisible and that cannot be weighed. But we have found again and again that even these minute quantities can be chemically identified with as much certainty as those isotopes that exist in weighable quantities. One of the proofs was the discovery of the fission of uranium itself, which was established because it became clear that the substances that had been thought to be isotopes of radium were active isotopes of barium, even though the existing concept concerning nuclear transformations declared fission to be an impossibility.

Because of the small quantities of artificial isotopes, all customary chemical means of identification must be discarded. Proof of the presence of these substances is established solely by means of the ionizing radiation (beta or gamma rays) that is emitted by radioactive atoms. And since the radiation sources available in Germany for these isotopes are not very powerful, the electroscopes that are used for measuring the activity of

---

[1] Some of the isotopes of barium, lanthanum, strontium, and yttrium that are listed have not yet been described in the literature; their existence has been proved by Hahn and Strassmann.

TABLE I B

Fragments resulting from the fission of
uranium-238, known in December 1941

Mass:	44 Ru	45 Rh	46 Pd	47 Ag	48 Cd	49 In	50 Sn
>105	$4^h \rightarrow 34^h \rightarrow$		?				
111				$26^m \rightarrow 7.5^d \rightarrow$ stable			
112				$17^h \rightarrow 3.2^h \rightarrow$ stable			
(113)					50^m		
					↓		
					stable		
115					$56^h \rightarrow 272^m$		
						↓	
						stable	
117					$170^m \rightarrow 117^m$		$\rightarrow$ stable

naturally radioactive elements are usually worthless for this kind of work. In practically every case one has to rely on methods of counting the emitted particles. This is done best and most simply with the Geiger-Müller counter, which has proved itself to be of inestimable value for the investigation of artifically radioactive elements. The method, then, consists in counting a certain unchangeable percentage of the particles emitted in a unit of time. This produces "activity curves" from which conclusions about the substances under investigation—for example, their half-lives, their complexity or lack of it—can be drawn.

Preliminary Experiments

To illustrate the method of investigation a few examples must be cited.

Curve A in Figure II-1 represents the activity of an uranium preparation (natural decay products removed) that has been irradiated for a short time by a weak neutron source, a radium-beryllium tube. The straight-line increase that can be read off the curve is due to the formation of new uranium-X

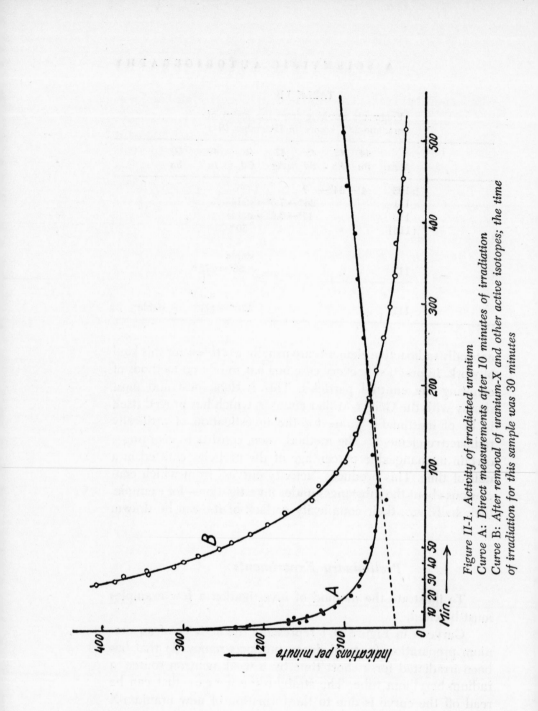

Figure II-1. Activity of irradiated uranium
Curve A: Direct measurements after 10 minutes of irradiation
Curve B: After removal of uranium-X and other active isotopes; the time
of irradiation for this sample was 30 minutes

which emits beta rays. The drop in activity in the left-hand portion of the curve is due to changes in activity of the "artificial" isotopes of unknown chemical nature that resulted from the neutron bombardment. Curve B of the same diagram represents a step forward. Using hydrogen sulfide to precipitate an element acting as the carrier for artificially radioactive isotopes, these elements have been separated from the uranium. As a result the confusing beta-ray emission of newly formed uranium-X has been eliminated.

But even curve B does not yet yield much information; it could result from a uniform substance or from a mixture of several substances. A method of checking this point is based on the known fact that uniform radioactive substances decay in such a manner that for a given unit of time the same percentage of the substance is changed. If you enter measured activities logarithmically on a diagram and enter the time lapse arithmetically, you obtain a straight line for the decay of a uniform substance. This has been done for the hydrogen-sulfide precipitation in curve A in Figure II-2. The representation is a curve at first but then becomes a straight line. If you subtract the extrapolated values for the straight line from the curved line you also obtain a straight line. Evidently we have a mixture of two isotopes, one with a half-life of about 60 minutes and one with a half-life of about 16 minutes.[2]

In reality there are still other isotopes in that precipitate. If the neutron bombardment lasts only a very short time and the measurements are made within minutes, the 16-minute substance is found to be accompanied by a shorter-lived substance of about 2 minutes half-life, while the 60-minute substance does not yet show (Figure II-3).[3] But if the irradiation lasts several hours or days, the 60-minute substance is accompanied by a 3-day substance (Figure II-4), and if the irradiation lasts weeks or months an additional substance with a half-life of about 60

[2] O. Hahn, L. Meitner, and F. Strassmann in *Berichte der Deutschen Chemischen Gesellschaft,* vol. 69, p. 905, 1936.

[3] O. Hahn, L. Meitner, and F. Strassmann in *Die Naturwissenschaften,* vol. 26, p. 475, 1938.

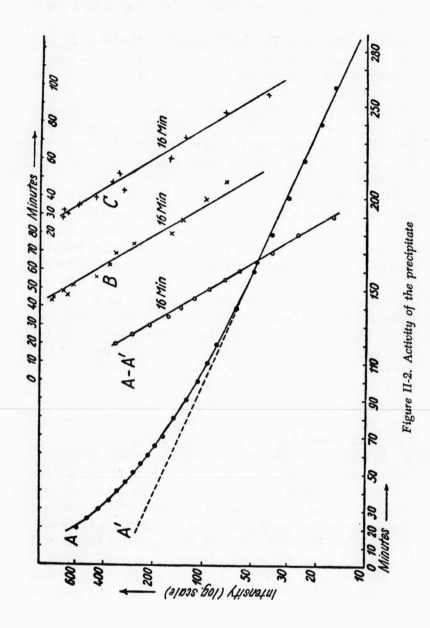

Figure II-2. Activity of the precipitate

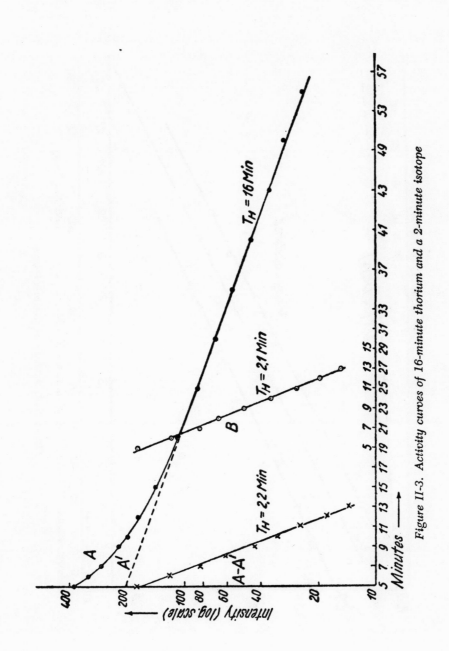

Figure II-3. Activity curves of 16-minute thorium and a 2-minute isotope

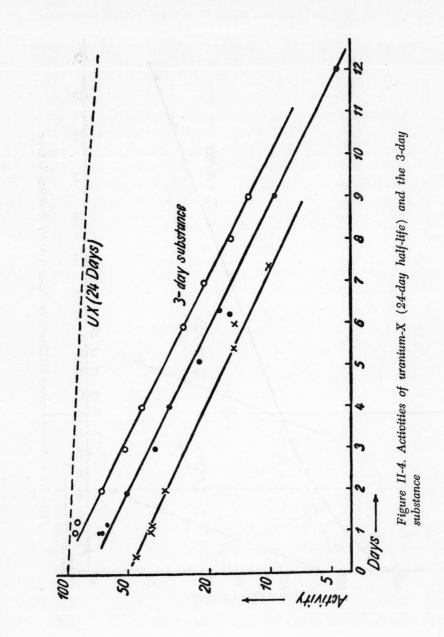

Figure II.4. Activities of uranium-X (24-day half-life) and the 3-day substance

days appears (Figure II-5). The investigation of such long-lived substances is comparatively simple if their activity is high enough. These substances are left over after the others have decayed completely. But this still does not tell anything about the chemical nature of these substances except for the fact that they belong to those elements that can be precipitated from an acid solution by H_2S. But it may mean that the substance was formed by the precipitated elements after precipitation. The final identification has to be done via a chemical analysis.

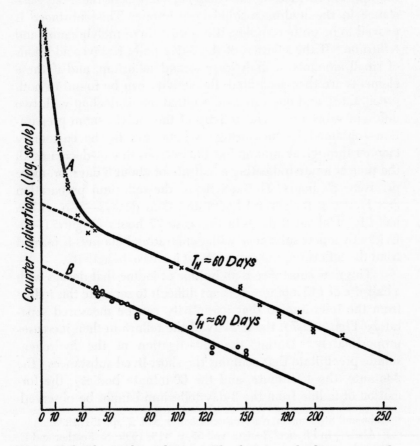

Figure II-5. The 60-day substance. The figures at the bottom give the duration in days

Chemical Investigation of
an Apparently Uniform Substance

It would be dangerous to conclude that a more or less straight line in the diagram must represent a uniform substance. Conclusions based on the shape of such exponential curves are not too precise, and a mixture of isotopes with half-lives that do not differ much can produce a deceptively uniform curve. An example is provided by the chemical analysis of the 3-day substance in the hydrogen-sulfide precipitate. This substance is proved to be quite complex; it is a mixture of molybdenum and tellurium.[4] If the solution of the 3-day body receives additions of small amounts of molybdenum and tellurium, and if these elements are then separated, the activity can be found in both precipitates, and one can soon see that one is dealing with two different substances. The activity of the molybdenum preparation—obtained by measuring its beta rays in the customary manner through aluminum foil 100 microns thick—decreases all the time at a rate indicating a half-life of about 3 days, or, more precisely, 67 hours. The activity of the tellurium preparation first increases for several hours and then decays—also with a half-life of about 3 days, in this case 77 hours (Figure II-6). Evidently a new substance with penetrating beta rays is formed from the tellurium, causing a strong increase in activity.

This new substance is an isotope of iodine that decays with a half-life of 140 minutes. It is not difficult to separate this iodine from the tellurium so that its activity can be measured separately (Figure II-7); the activity of the tellurium then increases proportinately.[5] During the investigation of the hydrogen-sulfide precipitate that contains the short-lived substances (the 2-minute, the 16-minute, and the 60-minute bodies), the formation of iodine from the 3-day tellurium cannot be observed.

[4] Hahn and Strassmann, *Naturwissenschaften*, vol. 27, p. 451, 1939.
[5] P. Abelson in *Physical Review*, vol. 55, p. 418, 1939; N. Feather and E. Bretscher in *Nature*, vol. 143, p. 516, 1939; O. Hahn and F. Strassmann in *Die Naturwissenschaften*, vol. 27, p. 451, 1939.

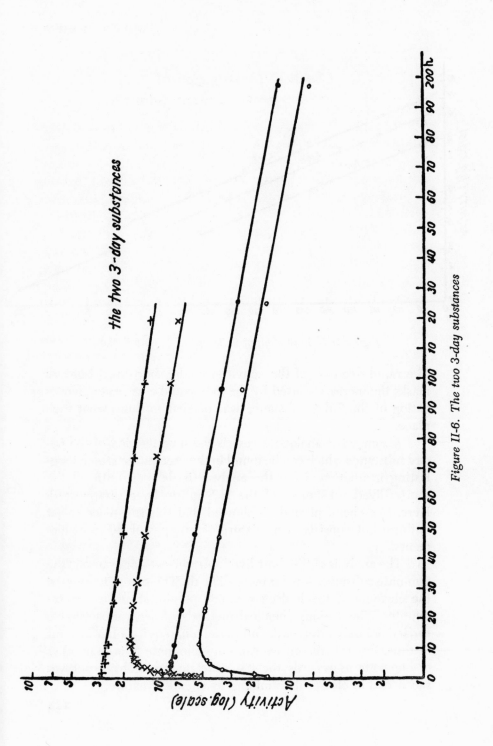

Figure II-6. The two 3-day substances

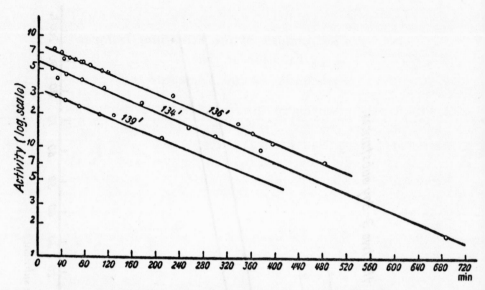

Figure II-7. Formation of iodine from 3-day tellurium

The rapid decrease of the activities of the short-lived isotopes masks the increase caused by the iodine and a separate investigation of the 3-day substance was needed to show what took place.

A somewhat analogous case is the investigation of the 60-day substance which can be found in the precipitate after a long-lasting irradiation. Here the analysis is delayed until all the shorter-lived substances of the H_2S group have disappeared. Here, too, chemical analysis showed that this substance is not uniform but consists of a mixture of isotopes of different elements.

The analysis of the short-lived substances—for example, the 2-minute substance—is far more difficult. The precipitation and the cleaning of the hydrogen-sulfide precipitate takes several minutes. The various chemical methods of separation can be carried out only afterward, and these, too, require a fair amount of time. For this reason we can only eliminate a large number of elements as regards the 2-minute body; we have not yet succeeded in clearly determining its chemical nature.

The Analysis of the Strontium Isotopes as an Example of the Systematics of the Procedure

After the preceding remarks, which apply to many different kinds of precipitates, a special group of elements may be selected to show details of the analysis.

An important group of isotopes in the case of uranium fission are those of the alkaline-earth metals barium and strontium. Isotopes of the closely related metal calcium apparently were not formed. Attempts to disentangle the various values of half-lives of the barium and strontium isotopes which are all precipitated together would be even less successful than with the case of the H_2S precipitation just described. But the investigation is aided because barium as well as strontium can be separated from uranium, uranium-X, and other fission products easily and rapidly.

As an example, we shall discuss the work with strontium; in the case of barium the situation is quite similar but a little harder for a nonchemist to understand.

The first experiments are quite similar to those described for the metals that can be precipitated with hydrogen sulfide, the advantage being that in the work with strontium we are dealing with one element only. Again the uranium was irradiated for different durations and the artificial strontium isotopes that had been formed were precipitated as quickly as possible. It was rather easy to find three strontium isotopes of different half-lives.[6] Figure II-8 shows the activity curve of a strontium preparation obtained from uranium that had been irradiated for 16 minutes. The activity decreases quickly at first but then rises very slowly. A weak maximum is reached after 3½ to 4 hours and then a slow decrease follows. If the weak rise is extrapolated to zero time and these values are subtracted from the experiment's curve, one obtains curve (c). It shows an

[6] C. Lieber, *Die Naturwissenschaften*, vol. 27, p. 421, 1939.

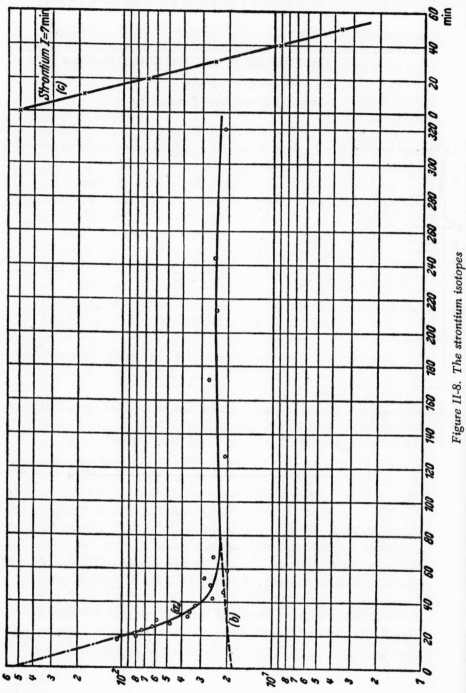

Figure II-8. The strontium isotopes

exponential decrease with a half-life of 7 minutes, indubitably an isotope of strontium. But the slowly decreasing curve has not yet been explained. It could belong to another strontium isotope which, in decaying, produces an active yttrium isotope. Or it could belong to an yttrium isotope with a zirconium isotope as the product.

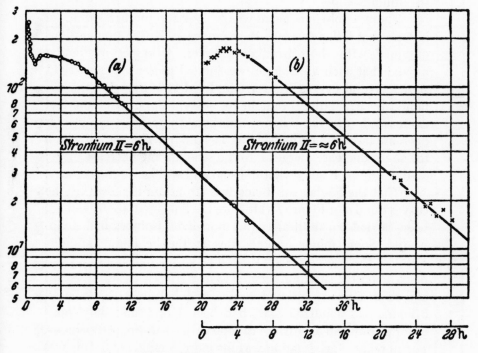

Figure II-9. *Activity of strontium-II*

Figure II-9 shows that the first assumption was the correct one. The uranium had been irradiated for several hours. Curve (a) again shows the decrease after the immediate separation of the strontum; curve (b) shows the activity of strontium that was not separated until about 1 hour after the irradiation had been stopped. By this time the 7-minute isotope had disappeared but a clearly visible increase in activity was present. Here we have a second isotope of strontium which obviously formed an yttrium isotope of a shorter half-life; both isotopes then decayed together. Figure II-10 shows the decrease of the activity of an yttrium isotope that had been separated from the strontium, proving that our conclusion had been correct. The half-life of this yttrium isotope is 3½ hours; the half-life of 6 hours of its mother substance indicates that this was probably a strontium isotope.

The next obvious move was to look for another strontium isotope that failed to make its presence known in preparations obtained with short irradiation times. A longer irradiation proved that such an isotope was indeed present. Figure II-11 shows several curves from a long-lived strontium isotope obtained by irradiating uranium for several days. After the fast decrease due to the 6-hour strontium, there follows a slower decrease indicating a half-life of 54–55 days. The way in which the sharp decrease merges into the straight-line decrease of the 55-day isotope is somewhat unusual and will be discussed later.

That the 55-day substance was strontium is shown by the curves c and d of Figure II-11. Here the final separations had not been carried out until after the short-lived isotopes had disappeared. Some minor irregularities at the beginning are discounted, the decrease fits a substance with a half-life of 55 ± 3 days. So far the situation seemed to be perfectly straightforward and clear. Three strontium isotopes, with half-lives of 7 minutes, 6 hours, and about 55 days, had been found, and the 6-hour isotope produced an yttrium isotope with a half-life of 3½ hours. But in reality the situation was far more complicated. This was discovered by using more powerful radiation sources and by irradiating uranium (with the weaker sources) for periods of several months. Both the "6-hour isotope" and the long-lived isotope turned out to be complex substances.

Let us look at the 6-hour isotope first. It had seemed somewhat odd that the increase in radiation, caused by the 3.5-hour yttrium, was so weak. This could be explained, of course, by assuming that the radiation from the yttrium was rather weak so that its beta rays did not influence the counter much through its 100-micron aluminum window. But a curve of the rays from

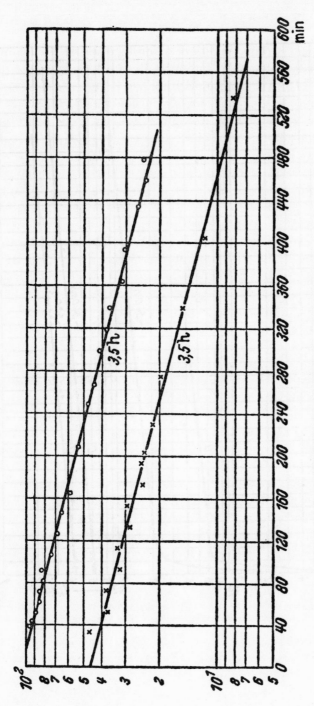

Figure II-I0. Activity of a 3.5-hour yttrium

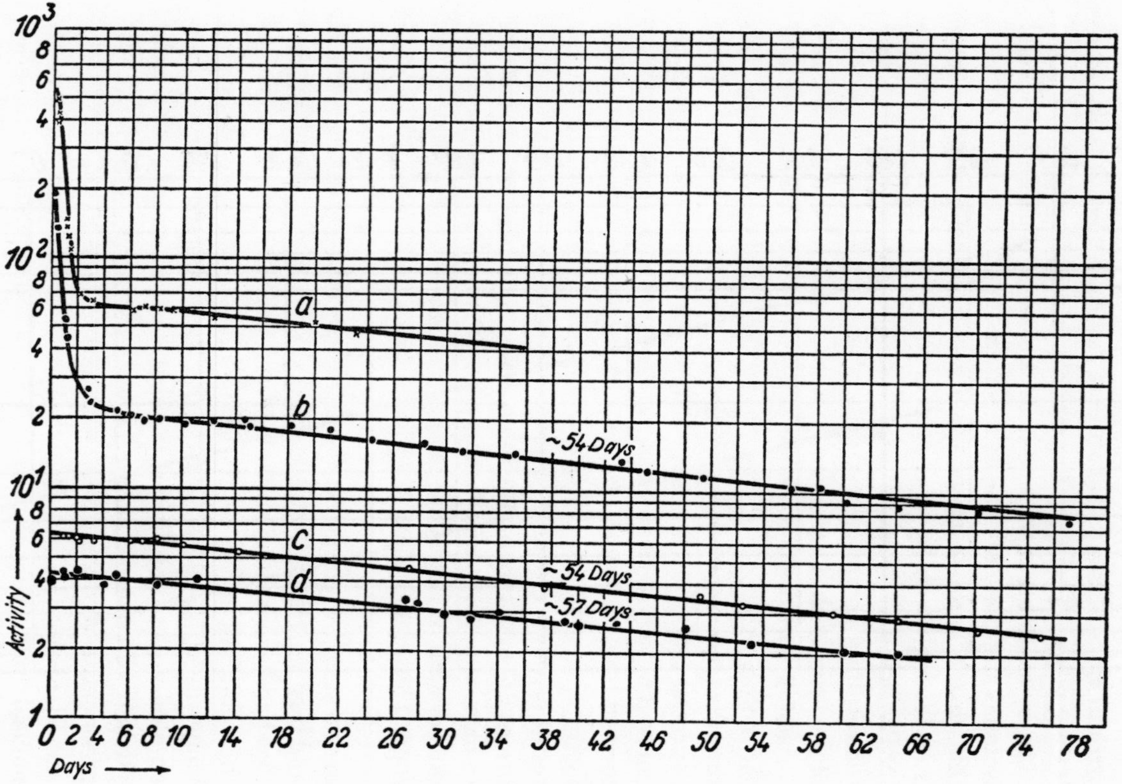

Figure II-11. The 55-day strontium

yttrium alone showed that its beta rays had considerable penetrating power. The weak increase could still be explained, however, by assuming that the 6-hour substance consisted of several isotopes and that only one of them produced yttrium.[7] To check this idea, a uranium preparation was irradiated with neutrons from the high-voltage equipment of the Kaiser Wilhelm Institute for Physics. The strontium was then separated and purified, and the resulting powerful preparation was treated for the removal of the yttrium that had been formed every 2 hours. We obtained a sheaf of curves the decrease of which had to be at the rate of the mother substance of the yttrium that had been removed. But this decrease showed a half-life of 2.7 hours instead of the expected 6 hours. The curves labeled A (from 1 to 9) and the curve B in Figure II-12 show the results. The 3.5-hour yttrium is formed by a strontium isotope with a half-life of 2.7 hours. The figure of 6 hours that had been obtained earlier had to be the result of the presence of at last two isotopes. One, with a half-life of 2.7 hours, had now been determined; the other one had to have a half-life longer than 6 hours, since both together produced a curve that had seemed to originate with a 6-hour isotope. This longer-lived isotope—it has a half-life of 8.5 hours—was then found. It can be detected easily in a highly active preparation by permitting the 2.7-hour isotope to disappear first, and then separating the longer-lived strontium from the yttrium that had been formed and measuring its activity separately. One then obtains curves due to the 8.5-hour strontium and the still-longer-lived 55-day strontium. At the same time the 8.5-hour strontium was found to be the mother substance of the 57-day yttrium discovered earlier. But the 8.5-hour strontium also produces an yttrium isotope with a half-life of 50 minutes [8] (Figures II-13 and II-13A). Whether these two yttrium isotopes are nuclear isomers formed by the 8.5-hour strontium, or whether this 8.5-hour strontium is a mixture of two isotopes with similar

---

[7] H. Götte, *Die Naturwissenschaften*, vol. 29, p. 496, 1941.

[8] O. Hahn and F. Strassmann, *Die Naturwissenschaften*, vol. 28, p. 543, 1940.

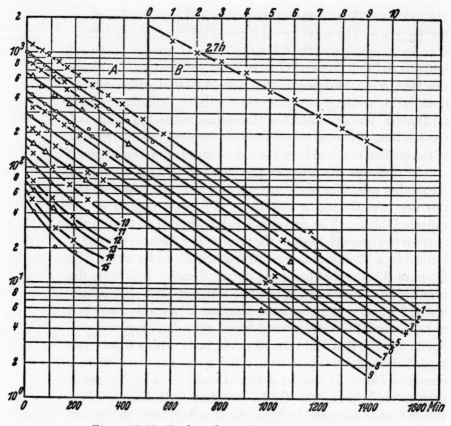

Figure II-12. Finding the 2.7-hour strontium isotope

half-lives, one forming the long-lived yttrium and the other the short-lived yttrium, has not yet been ascertained.

We now proceed to the 55-day strontium. In Figure II-11 we showed a number of curves for strontium that had been formed by uranium after several days of irradiation. These curves showed small anomalies at the beginning of the straight line representing the decay of the 55-day isotope. There seemed to be a small increase in activity that did not look like an experimental error. If the yttrium was again removed from the 55-day strontium the former showed a weak but definite activity which did not go with the 55-day period of its assumed mother sub-

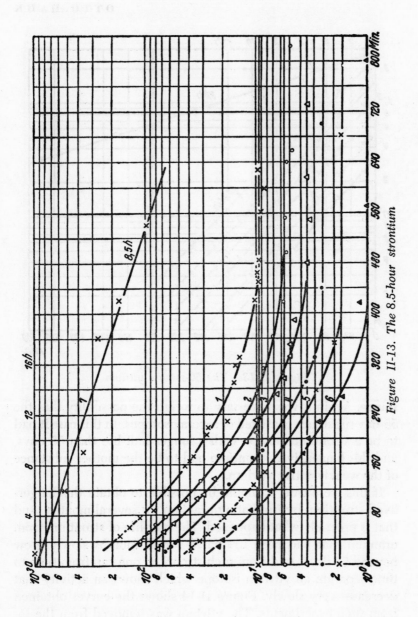

Figure II-13. The 8.5-hour strontium

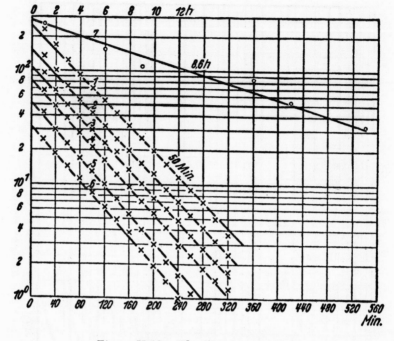

Figure II-13a. The 50-minute yttrium

stance. Again it was necessary to weigh the possibility that the 55-day substance consisted of several isotopes. In this case it had to be a strontium isotope with a longer half-life than 55 days, and this longer-lived strontium had to be the mother substance of the weakly active yttrium.

If this were true, it should be possible to obtain this longer-lived strontium by irradiating uranium for several months. And that is precisely what happened. The half-life of strontium from uranium that had been irradiated for 11 months slowly grew beyond 55 days. And from such strontium one can from time to time separate an yttrium isotope which shows an activity that decreases very slowly. Figure II-14 shows the curves obtained from such experiments. The yttrium was removed from the so-called 55-day strontium after the decrease had been watched for about 1 month. After the yttrium had been removed, the decay of the strontium was continuously measured as before, using the

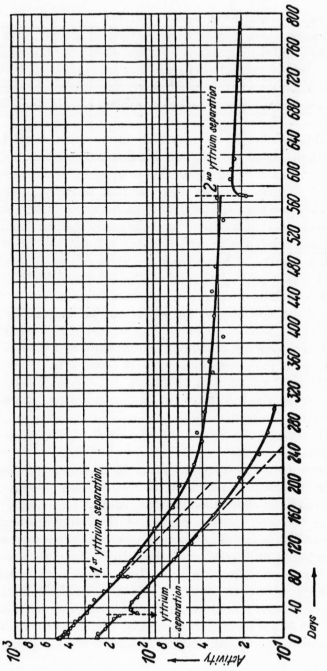

Figure II-14. *Proof of the complexity of 55-day strontium*

same experimental arrangement and the same counter. The lower curve shows that activity dropped off sharply after the separation and then increased for a few days. Then it decreased in a normal manner but after some time it could clearly be seen that the decrease was somewhat slower than was to be expected for a 55-day half-life—the broken line shows what it should have been.

All this shows even more clearly in the upper curve. Here the yttrium was removed for the first time after 80 days, but the continued measuring of the strontium showed that the decrease in activity proceeded more slowly as time went on. After 570 days, counting from the beginning of the experiment, the yttrium was removed once more, and the newly purified strontium shows a clear increase in activity. Since a 55-day isotope would show an activity of less than one-thousandth of its original activity after such a long period, the substance has to be a hitherto unknown strontium of very long half-life. This isotope produces the weakly radiating yttrium which, in our estimate, has a half-life of about 60 hours. These experiments proved that the 55-day strontium obtained from uranium is not a uniform substance but that, depending on the duration of the irradiation of uranium, it contains an increasing percentage of a longer-lived isotope. The half-life of this isotope is not yet known but it is certainly longer than 2 years.

The real 55-day strontium is evidently identical with a strontium isotope of mass 89 that had been obtained from natural strontium. The active strontium-89 then forms the stable yttrium-89. The other strontium isotopes all first produce active yttrium isotopes which then turn into zircon.

But the active yttrium formed by the 7-minute strontium was not actually known. Only very recently did we succeed in demonstrating its existence with the aid of the far more powerful neutron sources of the Max Planck Institute. Before, the search for the probably not very short-lived product of the 7-minute isotope had been practically hopeless. A very short irradiation period could not be used, because that would have resulted in weak strontium preparations. For the same reason comparatively large amounts of uranium had to be irradiated, but then the separation and purification of the strontium took so much time that most of the 7-minute isotope disappeared and the longer-lived isotopes interfered with the investigation.

With the more powerful neutron source the period of irradiation could be reduced to a few minutes and, by using a simple trick, almost any amount of uranium could be processed for the wanted isotope. We used, say, 50 grams of uranium nitrate dissolved in ether with a little water added. By shaking the solution repeatedly we removed the uranium-X. The solution was then irradiated and shaken again; the small amount of water then contained not only traces of uranium, but most of the fission products—including the strontium, which could then be separated from the other fission products, including the chemically similar barium isotopes.

The curve of strontium that had been formed during an irradiation lasting 4 minutes looked very much like the curve in Figure II-8. But because of the short and potent irradiation the activity is due mainly to the 7-minute isotope, and one could hope to find an active yttrium other than the 3.5-hour yttrium. In order to obtain it, the yttrium was separated from the strontium after 20 minutes and its activity measured. After a slightly more rapid beginning, the curve settled down to become a straight line corresponding to a half-life of about 9 hours.

But if the yttrium was removed from the strontium after 1 hour and this was repeated another 2 hours later, the activity of yttrium decreased more rapidly. Since its activity was weak, it was difficult to be certain of the half-life, but it seemed to be on the order of 3.5 hours. This result was corroborated by another irradiation of the uranium, lasting 16 minutes. During this period a larger percentage of the 2.7-hour strontium was formed, and the strontium produced more yttrium with a half-life of 3.5 hours. However, even in this experiment the presence of the new 9-hour yttrium could be detected after about 20 minutes, during which time most of the 7-minute strontium had disappeared. A second separation of yttrium from the strontium showed that it was, for the most part, the 3.5-hour yttrium.

These results are shown in Figure II-15. Curve *a* shows the activity of the yttrium separated from the strontium after 20 minutes; curve *b* that of the yttrium obtained later. Curves *c* and *d* are those of the strontium obtained by longer irradiation. Because the longer-lived strontium isotopes were present in larger quantities, the decrease of curve *c* is more pronounced than that of curve *a*.

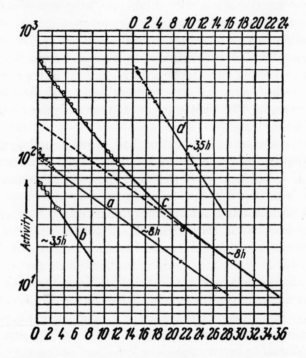

Figure II-15. The formation of 8-hour yttrium from 7-minute strontium.

These experiments lead to the conclusion that the 9-hour yttrium is formed by the short-lived strontium isotope. Once the latter has decayed, which is the case after about 1 hour, the longer-lived strontium isotope produces only the 3.5-hour yttrium, with traces of the 50-minute and 57-day isomers. Even if the 9-hour activity is extrapolated to zero time and the calculated values are subtracted from the measured values, a pure

234

3.5-hour curve is still not obtained; the decrease at the beginning is too strong. This may indicate the existence of still another unknown yttrium isotope, which would mean, in turn, that the 7-minute strontium is not a pure isotope either.

This summary of the various methods has shown how we established the existence of five different active isotopes of strontium and the products, the yttrium isotopes.

But the problem is not yet completely solved even for this one element. We still don't know yet whether these strontium isotopes are primary fission products or whether they are already the results of other transformations. Since uranium fission also yielded a number of barium isotopes, one had to assume that strontium and xenon, as well as barium and krypton, are formed simultaneously. The atomic numbers of both pairs of elements— 38 + 54 and 56 + 36, respectively—add up to 92, the atomic number of uranium. In one of the first reports on uranium fission the formation of xenon had been stated,[9] and soon afterward Krypton was found by Dutch [10] and American [11] researchers as well as by us.[12]

The first method we used for finding the noble gases was the following: While the irradiation of a uranium solution was going on, air was blown through the solution and then collected in a container with chilled adsorption coal. This coal was then tested for the presence of alkali and alkaline-earth metals. If such metals were found they had to have formed in the coal from an active noble gas, since neither of the metals themselves nor their salts would be carried along by the air. This method produced several cesium, barium, and rubidium isotopes.

Active strontium isotopes could be found only after a new method had been introduced which relied on the "emanation capability" of uranium salts for a quick determination of the

[9] O. Hahn and F. Strassmann, *Die Naturwissenschaften,* vol. 27, p. 163, 1939.

[10] F. A. Heyn, A. H. W. Aten, and C. J. Bakker, *Nature,* vol. 143, pp. 516 and 679, 1939.

[11] A. Langsdorf, Jr. *Physical Review,* vol. 56, p. 205, 1939.

[12] Hahn and Strassmann, *op. cit.,* p. 529.

presence of active noble gases.[13] The gases produced by irradiation will diffuse out of the preparation and their products can be collected on a negatively charged electrode. It is possible to remove the active deposits from the electrode in fractions of a minute and to separate them chemically. This method yielded six cesium and rubidium isotopes, several barium isotopes, and the 2.7-hour, the 8.5-hour, and the 55-day strontium isotopes which had been formed by krypton isotopes.[14] It may be added here that we later succeeded in separating the xenon and krypton isotopes immediately. This was done by having two adsorption containers in series. The first one was chilled with solid carbon dioxide and alcohol, the second with liquid air. The xenon isotopes were adsorbed in the first of these containers; the krypton isotopes were caught by the lower temperature of the liquid air.

Using the powerful neutron source of the Max Planck Institute we have recently succeeded in proving that the 7-minute strontium isotope is produced by a krypton isotope. Earlier attempts to find it by way of the emanation method had been unsuccessful; presumably the amount of 7-minute strontium had been too small in comparison with the longer-lived isotopes, even with the shortest irradiation period that could be used. The conclusion must be that the krypton isotope which forms the 7-minute strontium has an especially short half-life. In agreement with the proof that the 7-minute strontium forms an yttrium isotope of about 9 hours half-life, we found this new yttrium isotope also in the active deposit from strongly emanating uranium.

Whether the long-lived strontium with a half-life of more than 2 years is formed by a krypton isotope has not so far been proved.

As a result of the experiments that have been described we can now construct the following scheme for the strontium isotopes:

[13] O. Hahn and F. Strassmann, *Die Naturwissenschaften,* vol. 28, p. 54, 1940.

[14] *Op. cit.,* p. 455.

$$_{36}\text{Kr} \qquad _{37}\text{Rb} \qquad _{38}\text{Sr} \qquad _{39}\text{Y} \qquad _{40}\text{Zr}$$

? $\longrightarrow$? $\longrightarrow$ 7 min. $\longrightarrow$ 9 h. $\longrightarrow$?

very short $\longrightarrow$ 80 sec. $\longrightarrow$ 2.7 h. $\longrightarrow$ 3.5 h $\longrightarrow$ stable

? $\longrightarrow$? $\longrightarrow$ 8.5 h. $\Big\langle \begin{array}{l} \nearrow 57 \text{ days} \\ \searrow 50 \text{ min} \end{array}$ $\longrightarrow$?

2.5 min $\longrightarrow$ 15.4 min $\longrightarrow$ 55 days $\longrightarrow$ stable

> 2 years $\longrightarrow$ 60 h. $\longrightarrow$ stable

Since this discussion was restricted to the disentanglement of the strontium isotopes, their mother substances, and their follow-on products, the figures for the half-lives of the krypton and rubidium isotopes and their probable atomic weights have been deliberately omitted.[15] A discussion of the atomic weights of all fission products, as far as they can be determined, is planned in collaboration with Professor Mattauch.

Physical Changes in the Working Conditions as Means of the Investigation

It is not the purpose of this article to discuss in the same manner as strontium was discussed, the other groups of elements produced by uranium fission. This would amount to a repetition of all the chemical researches that have been done in this field. But it might be of interest to discuss the importance of a few systematical changes in the methods of irradiating uranium and the measurement of the fission products for the purpose of finding an explanation of the phenomena.

1. Duration of the Irradiation

One important point is the duration of the neutron bombardment of uranium. Once one has gained a certain amount of knowledge about the elements and isotopes to be expected, it

[15] More about the krypton-strontium group can be found in *Die Naturwissenschaften*, vol. 28, 1940, p. 451 (by W. Seelmann-Eggebert); p. 496 (by H. Götte); and p. 455 (by O. Hahn and F. Strassmann).

is possible to vary the duration of irradiation and also the time interval between irradiation and chemical separation of the elements formed. That way one can divide the often hopelessly mixed isotopes and secondary and tertiary products into groups that can be recognized. This research method was explained in the discussion of the preliminary experiments as well as in the discussion of the research on strontium isotopes.

2. Energy of the Neutrons used

The examples mentioned, and all the other fission processes that were investigated at the Kaiser Wilhelm Institute, are best released by slow neutrons. The radium-beryllium tubes, which, until quite recently, were our only neutron sources, were surrounded by paraffin, and the preparations to be irradiated were located at a distance of a few centimeters. Behind these preparations there were thick layers of paraffin. If the arrangement is precisely the same but no paraffin is used, the yield of fission products is much smaller. Slow neutrons proved to be most effective. But even when the most energetic neutrons that radium-beryllium tubes could produce were used, the chemical nature of the fission products was always the same.

This picture is changed when the neutrons are the very energetic neutrons that can be obtained by using deuterons on lithium with high-voltage equipment; their energies can be as high as 17 mev. Japanese researchers [16] were the first to discover, as was later corroborated by American researchers,[17] that these very energetic neutrons cause entirely different fission processes, resulting in isotopes of the elements ruthenium (no. 44), rhodium (no. 45), palladium (no. 46), silver (no. 47), cadmium (no. 48), and indium (no. 49). The fission processes caused by these energetic neutrons are more symmetrical than those caused by slow neutrons. No doubt the fission products observed earlier will also

[16] T. Yasaki, *Scientific Papers of the Institute for Physical-Chemical Research*, Japan, vol. 37, p. 457, 1940; Y. Nishina, T. Yasaki, K. Kimura, and M. Ikawa in *Physical Review*, vol. 58, p. 660, 1940, and vol. 59, pp. 323 and 677, 1941; also in *Nature*, vol. 146, p. 24, 1940.

[17] E. Segrè and G. T. Seaborg in *Physical Review*, vol. 59, p. 212, 1941.

be found when Li-D neutrons are used, because a high percentage of them are slow, too. In a few experiments on the symmetrical fission products with Li-D irradiation—using cadmium and boron—we found that the yield of symmetrical products compared to that of products of less symmetrical nature was about 1 : 1. If Li-D neutrons are used without slowing them down, the chemical analysis has to take into account the presence of *all* fission products.

Finally so-called resonance processes appear when uranium is irradiated. These processes involve the joining of one neutron of a certain energy level to the uranium nucleus (n, γ process),[18] or else the phenomenon that a second neutron leaves the nucleus together with the one that started the process ($n, 2n$ process).[19] In the former case the uranium isotope with a half-life of 23 minutes is formed; this isotope was known before uranium fission was discovered.[20] In the latter case an isotope with a half-life of 7 days is the result.[21] The 23-minute isotope then forms an isotope of element no. 93 with a half-life of 2.3 days.[22] One has to keep in mind when separating the various fission products that these isotopes might be present.

3. Intensity of the Radiation

It sounds trivial to say that a more intensive irradiation of uranium and the larger yield of fission products that results is preferable to weaker preparations. But it is quite instructive to show by way of an example how increased intensity of preparations leads to results that could not be obtained with weaker

[18] L. Meitner, O. Hahn and F. Strassmann in *Zeitschrift für Physik,* vol. 106, p. 249, 1937.
[19] Y. Nishina. T. Yasaki, K. Kimura, and M. Ikawa in *Physical Review,* vol. 57, p. 1182, 1940; T. Yasaki, *op. cit.;* E. McMillan in *Physical Review,* vol. 58, p. 178, 1940.
[20] O. Hahn, L. Meitner, and F. Strassmann, *Berichte der Deutschen Chemischen Gesellschaft,* vol. 69, p. 912, 1936.
[21] E. McMillan, *Physical Review,* vol. 58, p. 178, 1940.
[22] E. McMillan and P. H. Abelson in *Physical Review,* vol. 57, p. 529, 1939.

preparations. Let us use barium as such an example. We had established the existence of three isotopes with half-lives of 14 minutes, 86 minutes, and approximately 300 hours. The 14-minute and the 300-hour isotopes produce active isotopes of lanthanum, one with an estimated half-life of 2½ hours, the other with a measured half-life of 44 hours.[23] We suspected that the 14-minute barium was a primary fission product, while the others were known to be produced by xenon.[24]

As far as the 14-minute barium is concerned, our results had to be revised as soon as the high-voltage equipment of the Max Planck Institute furnished more intensively radiating preparations. It was found to consist of two different isotopes, each of which produced an active lanthanum isotope. The 86-minute barium isotope which was mixed with the so-called 14-minute isotope and the active lanthanum that was formed by the 14-minute barium produced a curve that was too complicated for a good explanation. Having the powerful new neutron source we proceeded as follows: The irradiation time was cut to a few minutes so that only very little 86-minute barium was formed, because this isotope is formed by a 7-minute cesium isotope which is itself the product of a 45-second xenon isotope.

Immediately after irradiation the barium was removed from the uranium and then dissolved. More solvent was added to obtain a larger volume. We then drew samples of a few cubic centimeters from this supply at 6-minute intervals; as time went on, the volume of the samples was slowly increased. A few milligrams of iron were then added to separate the barium from the lanthanum that had formed in the meantime. The barium was then precipitated quantitatively and measured over a period of 4 minutes. This, in each case, gave the activity of the barium isotopes still present, without interference from the lanthanum. By increasing the amount of barium from the solution and adding inactive barium in unchanging amounts it was possible

---

[23] O. Hahn and F. Strassmann, *Die Naturwissenschaften*, vol. 28, p. 543, 1940.

[24] Hahn and Strassmann, *op. cit.*, vol. 27, p. 529, 1939.

to obtain about the same reading for the activity each time. This avoided a gradual loss of precision in the readings, since the active barium naturally weakens as time goes on. Calculating from these readings for equal amounts of barium solution gives the actual decrease of the activity of the barium, without any perturbations from active follow-on products. The only correction needed was that for the small amount of 86-minute barium which would be present. But the curve for the so-called 14-minute barium was an actual curve and not a straight line, thus indicating that 14-minute barium was not a single substance. Calculations suggested the presence of two isotopes, one with a half-life of not quite 6 minutes and another with a half-life of about 18 minutes.

Another series of experiments concerned the lanthanum that was formed by these barium isotopes. Here the method consists in separating the lanthanum when the products of both barium isotopes are still present and separating the lanthanum once more after the 6-minute barium has decayed. After waiting for some time the lanthanum from the still-present 18-minute barium is separated and measured. These investigations are not yet finished, but it is certain that each of the short-lived barium isotopes forms a lanthanum isotope; the half-lives of the latter are about 70 minutes and 3.5 hours.

Still another result of the use of highly active preparations is the proof that the two short-lived barium isotopes are products of xenon isotopes. We found both barium isotopes on the negative electrode from emanation. That we had at first failed to find xenon as the mother substance of these barium isotopes—and therefore considered the "14-minute barium" a primary fission product—indicates that the xenon isotopes are so short-lived that only a small portion of them has time to escape from the uranium preparation before they themselves have decayed.

The investigation of the "14-minute barium" suggests that other isotopes now thought to be uniform may be mixtures, and there can be no doubt that more powerful neutron sources will reveal the existence of other fission products. Some of them may be the results of side chains, which applies to two bromium isotopes we have found.[25] Nothing speaks against the assumption that there are still more nuclear transformations which have intensities too weak to reveal their presence. But such side-chain reactions are certainly important for a complete understanding of the fission process.

4. Penetrating Power of the Radiation Used for the Investigations

One more point which is quite important in the investigation of the fission products is still to be mentioned—namely, checking on active substances by adding increasing thicknesses of metal foil between substance and counter and the comparison of the activities in counters with thin and with heavy walls. By the insertion of radiation-absorbing metal foil, only those atoms in mixed substances that emit especially penetrating beta rays will be measured. In that way we succeeded in finding isotopes which had not been noticed before. And by the use of counters with very thin walls—for example, 5 microns instead of the customary 100 microns—the easily absorbed beta rays can be measured and will reveal the presence of isotopes that cannot be detected with the 100-micron counter.

A few examples may be mentioned to illustrate both methods of investigation. Some time ago we proved the existence of a molybdenum isotope with a half-life of 18 minutes,[26] which is one of the uranium fission products. We then found an isotope of element no. 43 with a half-life of 14 minutes, which was formed by the 18-minute molybdenum. But the decrease of the activity of the molybdenum isotope always produced a straight line, no matter whether element no. 43 was present or had just been separated. This could be explained by assuming that the 18-minute molybdenum consisted of two isotopes, one of which is the mother substance of the isotope of element no. 43. In this case the combined activity of the mother isotope and of element

[25] O. Hahn and F. Strassmann, *Die Naturwissenschaften*, vol. 27, p. 529, 1939 and vol. 28, p. 817, 1940.
[26] Hahn and Strassmann, *Die Naturwissenschaften*, vol. 29, p. 369, 1941; and *Zeitschrift für Physik*, vol. 117, p. 789, 1941.

no. 43 would increase at first, while the activity of the other molybdenum isotope decreases steadily, just compensating the increase. After a number of failures the newly formed molybdenum isotopes were measured through aluminum foil of different thicknesses. As the thickness was increased, the figures for the half-life were gradually reduced from 18 minutes to 12 minutes. Using still thicker foil did not change the result further (see Figure II-16). This experiment proved the existence of a hitherto-unknown molybdenum isotope with a half-life of 12 minutes. There could be no confusion with the 14-minute isotope of element no. 43, for its production would have resulted in an apparent lengthening of the half-life instead of a shortening.[27] Furthermore, the beta rays of the 14-minute isotope were completely absorbed by 2 or 3 millimeters of aluminum.

In this example the addition of absorbing metal foils led to the discovery of a fission product with penetrating beta rays. Now for some examples of the value of thin-walled counters for measuring easily absorbed radiation. It has already been mentioned that neutron bombardment of uranium causes, in addition to fission, a resonance process and an $n, 2n$ process resulting in artificially active isotopes of uranium itself. One of these isotopes is the one that originated through an n, γ process with a half-life of 23 minutes. This results, as McMillan and Abelson have shown, in an active isotope of element no. 93 with a half-life of 2.3 days. The other uranium isotope is produced by very fast neutrons via the $n, 2n$ process. First discovered by Japanese researchers [28] and corroborated by Americans [29] it has a half-life of 7 days. The investigations by these researchers showed that the 2.3-day substance [an isotope of neptunium], as well as the 7-day uranium isotope, lacks penetrating beta rays; the same discovery was made by Starke for the 2.3-day substance.[30]

27 See also W. Maurer and R. Ramm, *Die Naturwissenschaften*, vol. 29, p. 368, 1941, and the literature cited in footnote 26.
28 Y. Nishina, T. Yasakii, K. Kimura, and M. Ikawa, *Physical Review*, vol. 57, p. 1182, 1940.
29 E. McMillan, *Physical Review*, vol. 58, p. 178, 1940.
30 K. Starke, *Die Naturwissenschaften*, vol. 30, p. 107, 1942.

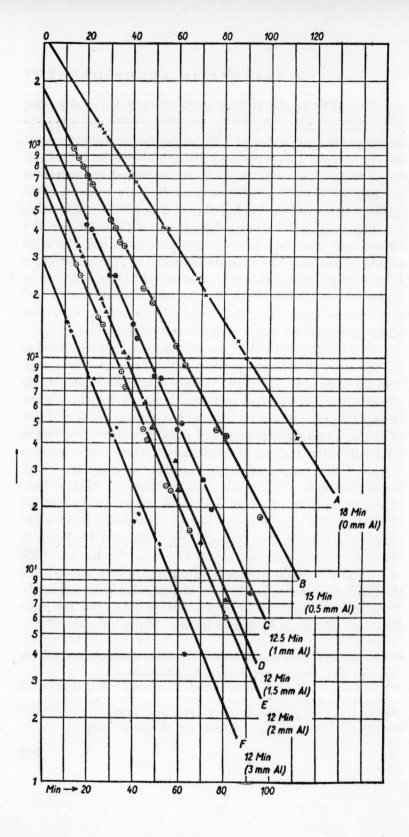

Detecting the presence of these bodies with the normal 100-micron counter is, therefore, difficult, unless one deals with high general activities. Here the superiority of the 5-micron counter is clear. Figure II-17 shows the diminishing activity of a mixture of the 23-minute uranium and the 2.3-day substance of approximately equal radiation intensity, as measured with the 5-micron counter, the 100-micron counter, and the latter with an extra 500 microns of aluminum. The preparations for these measurements came from the same solution, which, of course, contained a little ordinary uranium. The quantity used for the 100-micron counter was about twice that used for the 5-micron counter; for the measurement through 600 microns of aluminum a much larger quantity was used. The mild activities of the uranium present, and of the uranium-X which was formed by the uranium, were established for each sample and subtracted from the measured values. For purposes of comparison all values were calculated for equal amounts of the original solution. As can be seen in the diagram, curve A begins to straighten out fairly soon, indicating that we are dealing with roughly equal amounts of both substances. In curve B the 23-minute substance has the upper hand, but after 200 minutes it has decayed, and at that moment the activities of curves A and B show a ratio of 6 : 1, proving that the rays from the 2.3-day substance are absorbed much more easily than these from the 23-minute uranium isotope. In curve C the soft rays from the 2.3-day substance do not appear; this curve is representative solely of the decay of the 23-minute isotope.

Still more easily absorbed than the rays from the 2.3-day substance are the rays from the 7-day uranium isotope produced by irradiating uranium with very fast neutrons. The soft beta rays from this isotope fail to register in the normal 100-micron counter unless the over-all intensities are very high. But in the 5-micron counter the substance can be recognized without any difficulty and the decrease of its activity can be measured. But

---

Figure II-16. Proof of the complex nature of active molybdenum. Figures such as "3 mm Al" refer to the thickness of aluminum foil through which these readings were taken

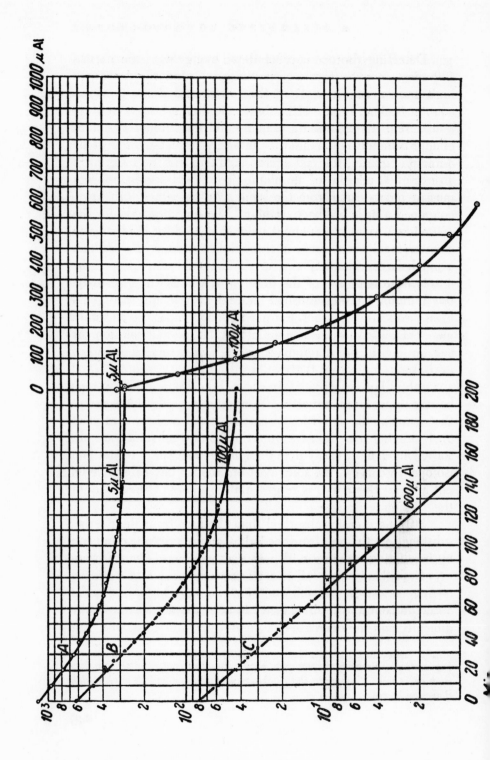

since the 7-day isotope is precipitated along with ordinary uranium and since the formation of uranium-X cannot be prevented,
measurements taken over a period of several weeks produced
very uncertain results. As in other experiments, a solution of the
7-day isotope with ordinary uranium was prepared and at
regular intervals a certain percentage was precipitated in the
form of uranium-sodium acetate which removed the uranium-X.
Carefully weighed samples of the precipitate, four equal samples at a time, were measured one after the other with the 5-
micron counter. The alpha rays from the uranium were eliminated by a layer of cellophane just thick enough to stop them.
Of course there was some spread in the readings, but this was
compensated for by taking four readings each time, at least as
long as the intensity of the 7-day isotope was still reasonably
high. Figure II-18 shows the results: the straight line is the
theoretical line for a half-life of 7 days, which can be seen to fit
the actual measurements satisfactorily. This was one more corroboration of the work done by the Japanese and American
researchers.

Although the 7-day isotope of uranium and the 2.3-day
isotope of neptunium are not, properly speaking, fission products, they are included in the discussion because they originate
during irradiation and their presence has to be taken into
account.

Final Remarks

This discussion of the physical changes in the working conditions is by no means complete. We have discussed only those
changes that proved helpful in our chemical investigations.
Physicists have many other ways of investigating the phenomena, as for example the Wilson cloud chamber, which permits

---

*Figure II-17. Suppression of the rays from 2.3-day eka-rhenium by alu-
minum foil. The curve on the right shows the absorption of radiation from
element no. 93; the figures at the top give the thickness of the aluminum
foil in microns.*

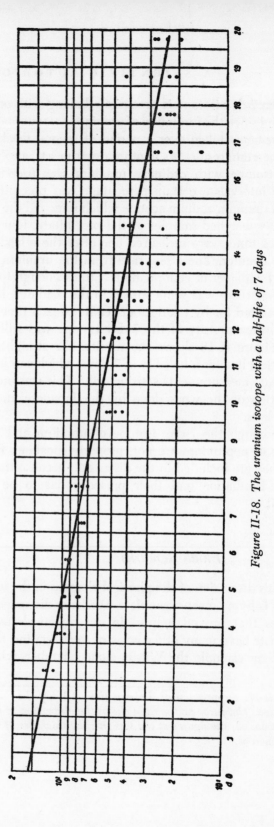

Figure II-18. The uranium isotope with a half-life of 7 days

statements about the energy of beta rays and their electric charge. And positive and negative charges can be established by using a magnetic field with the counter. Checking on the sign of the electric charge has proved useful for finding out whether a fission product is, or is not, identical with artificial isotopes obtained by conventional means.[31]

For a more detailed investigation of the radiation the beta-ray spectrometer can be used. This permits measuring the energy content of the rays emitted by various atoms in another manner than by measuring the absorption. This instrument also makes it possible to learn whether the electrons originated from the nucleus, thereby producing an element with a higher number, or whether an excited atom emits an electron line spectrum. If the gamma rays emitted are also investigated, the atomic number of the follow-on product can be determined and the possibility of a K electron capture investigated.

At this point it is not necessary to dwell on these methods of investigation, which have proved very successful in other countries—especially in the United States where powerful neutron sources are available. This report proposed to review the chemical investigation of the fission products. Of course a full understanding of all the fission phenomena can be reached only by complete collaboration between physics and chemistry. It is to be hoped that the number of powerful neutron sources in Germany will be increased so that the investigation of the fission phenomena can be extended in many directions.

[31] W. Bothe and A. Flammersfeld, *Die Naturwissenschaften*, vol. 29, p. 194, 1941.

APPENDIX III

The Chemical Separation of the Elements and Isotopes Produced by the Fission of Uranium.

BY OTTO HAHN AND FRITZ STRASSMAN

(Submitted to the Prussian Academy of Science by Mr. Grapow on the occasion of the Extraordinary Convention of November 23, 1944; originally published in the *Abhandlungen der Preussischen Akademie der Wissenschaften* (Jahrgang 1944, Mathematisch-naturwissenschaftliche Klasse No. 12) under the title *"Die chemische Abscheidung der bei der Spaltung des Urans entstehenden Elemente und Atomarten."*)

Preliminary Remarks

In a report on the fission products of uranium [reprinted here as Appendix II] it was shown by means of a number of examples how the activity curves of the preparations permit conclusions about the uniformity or complexity of the isotopes present and whether one is dealing with different isotopes of the same element or with sequences from radioactive decay. The multitude of strontium isotopes that are produced by fission, their mother substances, and follow-on products were used to describe the methods of disentanglement of all these isotopes. Finally it was mentioned how changes in the physical aspects of the experimentation and the methods for making measurements help to interpret the phenomena.

The methods for chemical purification of the elements were mentioned only occasionally and in passing.

Understanding of the many isotopes produced by fission is important not only as an end in itself; among the fission products there are many active isotopes that are useful for indicator experiments. A number of them cannot be produced at all—or at least have not been produced—with the customary methods of nuclear transformations; with some others there are advantages in making them through uranium fission instead of out of the same element or from neighboring elements. For all these reasons it is desirable to describe the chemical separation of the fission products and the methods of obtaining short-lived isotopes. These short-lived isotopes, since they are the probable first links in the decay chains, are of special interest if an understanding of all the processes is desired. But since they have short half-lives the methods for separating them differ from the well-established analytical methods because of the necessity for making the separations quickly.

It is desirable to precede the theme of this report with some statements about experiences with radioactive atoms that have been gathered mainly at the Kaiser Wilhelm Institute for Chemistry over the course of many years. Then we shall make some general statements about experimental work with uranium and about the separation of the noble gases, and give some hints about methods of analysis and their simplification and describe the treatments of the preparations and the measuring of their activities. A systematic description of the separation of the various elements and their isotopes will be the subject of a later report.[1]

[1] *Translator's Note.* Not published, and probably not written.

The Difference between Chemical and Radiochemical Methods

There is a difference in principle between the customary chemical methods of investigation and the methods of radiochemistry. In normal chemical reactions the unchanging stable elements are being investigated, and this usually requires several trillions of atoms or molecules. In radioactive research the investigation deals with atoms that are changing while they are being investigated, and the research is based on the measurement of the radiation emitted by the changing atoms. The clue is not the number of atoms present but the number of atoms that change within a unit of time. Since this is the case, the presence of radioactive elements can be detected with quantities that are far below the minimum needed for the recognition of ordinary chemical elements. In the case of radioactive elements the radiation emitted can be followed down to single atoms that send out rays or particles. This is possible because the particles from changing atoms possess very high energies. The ionization of gas molecules struck by such particles is sufficient to indicate a single particle in the Wilson cloud chamber or the Geiger counter.

Even minute quantities of an element retain their specific characteristics.

But if the detection methods are so sensitive, the question arises whether there is a lower limit at which the atoms of an element still retain their specific chemical characteristics. Do not the characteristic reactions cease to take place gradually? At this point it is useful to remember the experiments that led Hahn and Strassmann to the discovery of the fission of uranium atoms.

After irradiating uranium with neutrons a few artificially radioactive isotopes were found, which had to be considered radium isotopes. Only a few thousand atoms were involved,

253

weighing less than a trillionth of a gram. Barium, which is quite similar to radium, was used as carrier for these minute amounts. But our "radium" isotopes did not behave quite as could be expected of radium. We failed to separate them from barium even though we used methods that had been successful for many years in separating radium or its isotopes mesothorium and thorium-X from barium. In order to check whether the few thousand atoms of our artificially active isotopes failed to exhibit the chemical characteristics which large quantities would display, we made equally tiny amounts of the natural radium isotopes mesothorium and thorium-X. These small amounts behaved precisely as expected: they could be "enriched" in the form of chlorides and bromides and were not in the form of carbonates.

Then we mixed our weak artificial isotopes with our weak natural isotopes, repeated the fractionizations with barium, and saw that the natural radium could be separated from the barium, but the artificial isotopes could not be. Proof for the fission of uranium was thereby established.

These experiments also proved that the chemical characteristics of an element remain the same, even down to minimal concentrations.

The apparent exception with large-surfaced precipitates

If in the course of work with active isotopes we found what seemed to be deviations from the chemical nature of the element represented we could say that the inactive element, under the same conditions, would behave like the active isotopes which are merely much easier to trace. Such apparent exceptions are encountered from time to time.

As is well known, the salts of lead will not be precipitated by a surplus of a watery solution of NaOH but will be precipitated by ammonia. But if small quantities of ferric salts that contain the lead isotope thorium-B are precipitated with an NaOH solution, the active lead does not remain dissolved but is precipitated along with the iron hydroxide as if ammonia had been used. The iron-hydroxide precipitate has a large surface area and adsorbs the small amounts of lead. The same condition would exist if the lead were ordinary inactive lead. One can even check the adsorption capacity of the iron-hydroxide precipitates by slowly adding ordinary lead to the active isotope.

One method of separating uranium-X from uranium is based on a similar phenomenon. The method consists of precipitating uranium and iron hydroxide with ammonia in the form of ammonium uranate, then the uranate is treated with ammonium carbonate and dissolves again. One would expect the thorium isotope uranium-X that had been precipitated along with the iron to dissolve again because thorium hydroxide is soluble in ammonium carbonate. But it remains absorbed by the iron precipitate, though larger quantities of thorium hydroxide could be separated from iron in this manner.

One could probably separate a tiny quantity of a uranium isotope from larger quantities of thorium in the same manner; the uranium would stay adsorbed by the iron hydroxide while the thorium would be dissolved.

If the precipitates have a large surface area, are amorphous, or consist of microcrystals, one must always assume the presence of atoms that do not belong to the precipitate. The precipitate, therefore, always needs purification by reprecipitation. This is best done by adding the same substance that forms the impurity in the precipitate, but in its inactive form. This "dilutes" the activity of the impurity to such an extent that the amount of the active substance which is still adsorbed in the second precipitate no longer produces readings, or at least only very weak ones. Repetition of the process for the third time eliminates the presence of the impurity even in difficult cases. How much of the stable isotope has to be added depends on whether one wishes also to isolate the impurity. If this is the case the addition of too much of the stable isotope may interfere with the experiment.

One example for this type of laboratory work is the separation of the group of rare-earth elements from the group of alkaline-earth elements. The rare-earth elements can be precipitated with a few milligrams of iron as the carrier by adding ammonia which must be free of carbon dioxide. In order to prevent the simultaneous precipitation of active barium or strontium, 100 to 200 milligrams of barium or strontium, or both, are added. After this process is repeated the iron will be free of active alkaline-earth metals even if the ammonia was not completely free of carbonates. Then the separation of the rare earths in the iron can be begun, without one's having to worry about the formation of new yttrium and lanthanum from barium or strontium that was not completely removed.

The advantages of crystalline deposits

As distinct from the precipitates with a large surface area, which have just been discussed, crystalline precipitates have a small surface area and do not adsorb other isotopes to a large extent. A single precipitation is often enough to separate the active isotope with the salt of the stable isotope from a mixture of a number of active isotopes.

The separation of the numerous isotopes resulting from uranium fission is a fine example. The active barium isotopes can be precipitated with high purity from a solution of irradiated uranium in weak hydrochloric acid by concentrated hydrochloric acid after an addition of a weighable quantity of inactive barium. A second precipitation yields barium that is absolutely free of all other fission products, even uranium and its follow-on product uranium-X. The barium yield is admittedly incorrect quantitatively, but allowances can easily be made. If one did not use barium chloride, which dissolves slowly in concentrated hydrochloric acid, but used the customary barium sulfate that is insoluble in the acid, the barium sulfate which produces a large surface area would adsorb a large number of other artificial radioactive isotopes, including uranium and uranium-X. With barium sulfate the experiment simply would not work.

Similar precise methods of separation exist for cesium with cesium-silico-wolframate, for uranium with uranyl-sodium-acetate, for zirconium with zirconium oxychloride. In the last case the presence of active barium with weighable quantities of inactive barium is undesirable. During the precipitation of the oxychloride holding the active zirconium, barium would also be precipitated as its choride, and the precipitate would be a mixture containing active zircon as well as active barium.

The primary condition for these reactions which yield the pure isotopes only is the ability of the precipitate to form crystals. It is not even necessary that the active isotope that is to be precipitated along with strontium in strontium nitrate, cesium metal. It is sufficient that the active isotope can form mixed crystals with the carrier element; for example, barium can be precipitated along with strontium in strontium nitrate, cesium along with rubidium in rubidium-tin chloride, and element no. 93 with uranyl-sodium acetate.

The preparation of irradiated uranium for analysis.

Because of the weakness of the neutron sources available in Germany—especially when radium-beryllium tubes are used —the complete separation of the fission products from the uranium is an absolute necessity, mainly because of the steady formation of the beta-radiating uranium-X. Just 10 grams of uranium have a beta-ray emission due to uranium-X amounting to 1 million particles per minute. But the yield of fission products, when using 1 gram of radium plus beryllium as the neutron source, is at least three orders of magnitude smaller, even if the slowed-down neutrons strike the uranium preparation in the most efficient manner. In order to obtain fission products with useful intensities it may be necessary to irradiate rather large quantities of uranium, on the order of several hundred grams.

Depending on the amount of irradiated uranium, there are several ways along which one can progress. If there are several hundred grams of irradiated uranium, it is practical to have it in the form of its nitrate and it does not matter whether the uranium nitrate is irradiated when in solution or in the solid state. If the uranium nitrate is then crystallized repeatedly, the first fractions of each crystallization contain virtually no fission products, so that the larger portion of the uranium can be removed

257

in this manner. But in this procedure all the uranium-X is left in the solution with the fission products and must be separated later. The methods to be used depend on which one of the fission products has been given preference.

With small quantities of uranium the "ether method" is faster. The uranium is irradiated while it is in the form of the crystallized nitrate that contains crystal water. After irradiation it is dissolved in ether; about 10 cubic centimeters of ether are required for every 10 grams of uranium salts. This results in a watery solution (because of the crystal water) which contains practically all the fission products in addition to small amounts of uranyl-nitrate. By repeating the process with more ether and a little water, the yield of fission products can be increased, but the amount of uranium that has to be separated later also increases. In this manner one can separate about 90 percent of the uranium from the fission products in a short time—if the amount of uranium is small, in only a few minutes—but here, too, the uranium-X stays with the fission products.

For proceeding further there are three methods:

(1) The precipitation of the uranium in the form of sodium pyro-uranate by adding a watery solution of NaOH. This separates most of the artificial alkali and alkaline-earth metals from uranium and uranium-X.

(2) The precipitation of the uranium with ammonium in the form of ammonium pyro-uranate which is then changed into uranium ammonium-carbonate by dissolving the precipitate in ammonium carbonate. This separates the uranium from the active rare-earth elements, but the uranium-X remains with the rare earths.

(3) The precipitation of the uranium as uranyl-sodium-acetate from an acetic-acid solution with sodium acetate. This separates most of the uranium from all fission products, including uranium-X.

But the separation of the uranium is not necessary for a number of fission products, for example, all the metals that can be precipitated with H_2S. The alkaline earth metals barium and strontium can be obtained dirctly from the irradiated uranium preparation. To do this, the uranium is first converted into ammonium pyro-uranate by precipitating a uranium salt with ammonia. Then the result is irradiated and the barium is precipitated from a solution of the uranate in concentrated hydrochloric acid. For the precipitation of strontium (plus barium) uranyl-nitrate is used because here the precipitation works with a solution in concentrated nitric acid. Since these alkaline-earth metals can be obtained easily in a pure form, this also is a simple method for the derivation of the products of these metals: lanthanum, cerium, and yttrium.

Separation of the noble gases from uranium

A precise method for obtaining quite a number of fission products is based on the physical separation of the two noble gases xenon and krypton that are produced during the fission of uranium. They are removed from the uranium solution by air that is bubbled through the solution, either during the irradiation or immediately afterward. Then they can be measured directly, or else they can be adsorbed at very low temperatures and form their own decay products in the adsorption containers. By controlling the temperature during the adsorption it is possible to obtain a separation of krypton from xenon and, consequently, the follow-on products rubidium, strontium, and yttrium from cesium, barium, and lanthanum. Fission products with a very short half-life cannot be obtained in that manner because the investigation of the adsorption substances does take several minutes.

For obtaining very short-lived products from the noble gases there is another method which was developed from the "emanation method" first used at the Kaiser Wilhelm Institute for Chemistry. The uranium preparation is made to have such a large surface area that it, when dry, shows a high emanation capability. The noble gases that have been formed during irradiation will diffuse out of a salt with such a large surface area. Their decay products will then form invisible "active deposits" on a negatively charged metal electrode and can be removed from the metal by means of an acid. This method worked quickly enough to permit the finding of a cesium isotope with a half-life of 40 seconds and a rubidium isotope with a half-life of 80 seconds. This report is not the place to go into the details of the separation of the noble gases by physical removal.

In some respects the separation of the noble gases is quite similar to the separation of those fission products which, either in the form of their elements or in the form of chemical compounds, can be separated by distillation. This method applies to iodine, bromine, and even to some platinum metals.

The Difference in the Analytical Methods for Long-Lived and Short-Lived Isotopes

It has been pointed out that for larger quantities of irradiated uranium it is practical to remove the major part of the (unchanged) uranium before the true separation of the fission products is undertaken. This removal reduces the volume of the materials with which one has to work. But the amounts of uranium to be irradiated depend not only on the available neutron sources but also on the purpose of the experiment. If the purpose is only to demonstrate the presence of certain fission products small quantities of uranium can be used; large quantities are needed if the purpose is to produce known isotopes with high intensities, such as are needed for indicator experiments. If the purpose is to ascertain the chemical nature and the radioactive constants of one or several isotopes, one need not hesitate to add in weighable quantities the elements probably represented by the artificial isotopes. And if the substances do not have very short half-lives, the usual methods of analytical chemistry can be used.

But during the process of discovery and separation of fission products with short half-lives the well-tested analytical methods can be used very seldom. Unless one has extremely powerful neutron sources available, one usually has to perform the separations in such a manner that not more than four to five times the half-life of the isotope elapses, from the end of the irradiation to the beginning of the intensity measurements. Even after such a short interval only 3 to 6 percent of the original intensities are left to be the "intensities at the beginning" of the measurements. The method chosen for the separation has to conform to the conditions that the separation can be made as fast as possible, that the precipitation must be specific for the element in question, and that the precipitate must be insoluble in the solution from which it came. However, a truly quantitative precipitation cannot be accomplished under these conditions. But practice in carrying out the steps of such experiments enabled us to begin the measurement of a radioactively "pure" substance with a half-life of ½ to 1 minute 1½ to 2 minutes after the end of the irradiation period. It is obvious that in such cases the neutron source, the laboratory, and the measuring equipment must be in close proximity so that no time is lost because distances have to be covered.

If the problem consists in measuring the yields of certain transformations, one must know, of course, what percentage of the yield can be obtained with the fast separation methods. The determination of the yield can be made easily *after* the decay of the isotopes in question. One must know precisely the amount of the inactive isotope that was added to the active isotope of the same element; after the radioactive measurements have been made one can work at leisure on a chemical analysis that will determine the amount of the substance in the preparation. If, for example, barium was obtained from irradiated uranium and a known quantity of inactive barium was added and then precipitated as the chloride and measured after precipitation, the yield can be found later by precipitating the preparation in the form of barium sulfate. Other elements are treated in an analogous manner.

Some Simplifications of the Analysis

It has already been pointed out that a crystalline deposit will contain not only the precipitated element and its active isotopes but also the isotopes of such elements as can form mixed crystals with the precipitated element. If fairly large quantities of strontium are precipitated in the form of its nitrate, the tiny amounts of active barium isotopes that might be present will be co-precipitated in the mixed crystals. After purification of the strontium precipitate, the active barium can be separated by the addition of small amounts of inactive barium in the form of barium chromate. This indirect method of barium separation is advisable if the active barium is desired in a highly concentrated form. Though the direct precipitation of the barium as its chloride is simpler, the fact that the chloride is soluble even in concentrated hydrochloric acid will result in having too much of the desired active isotopes remain in the solution.

Reversing the method, one can obtain the strontium isotopes in highly concentrated form by making a barium precipitate and later adding a very small amount of strontium and making a strontium barium separation.

Still another example of utilizing the formation of mixed crystals is the separation of element no. 93 from uranium which resembles it chemically. When oxidized, element no. 93 shows six valences and can be precipitated in mixed crystals with uranyl-sodium-acetate. It thus can be freed of the fission products of uranium. But when element no. 93 shows only four valences, it no longer forms mixed crystals with the uranyl salts and can therefore be separated.

Though precipitates consisting of comparatively large crystals produce pure preparations quite rapidly, one does not need to rely exclusively on such precipitates. In the important case of the separation of the beta-ray emitting thorium isotope uranium-X from the rare-earth isotopes, it would not be advisable to add weighable quantities of thorium because thorium is also radioactive. Hence zirconium, which is similar chemically in many respects, is chosen instead of thorium to be the carrier of the uranium-X. If, after separation of the rare-earth isotopes, the active zircon isotopes are to be separated from the uranium-X, one selects a chemical reaction in which the behavior of zirconium and thorium is dissimilar; the carrier for the thorium could then be a stable rare-earth isotope.

There are naturally a number of similar cases but, generally speaking, it is not difficult to find a way of separating an isotope that is present in very small amounts by simply adding a larger amount of an inactive isotope of an element that is chemically similar but not identical. The inactive element, carrying the active isotope, can then first be removed from all the other unwanted isotopes. After that an additional separation of the active isotope from its inactive carrier must be made.

It is obvious that among the multiple products of uranium fission some elements can be easily obtained in a radioactively pure form, while this is much more difficult with others. The separation of the rare earth elements from uranium-X and from one another especially requires much experience and is always time-consuming, because they almost always show precipitates with large surface areas and therefore with the ability to absorb active impurities. In this situation it is quite pleasing that the rare-earth metals are the decay products of the alkaline-earth metals that can be obtained easily in the form of fairly large crystals. In all cases where the mother substances—for example barium and strontium—do not have a very short half-life compared with the half-lives of the decay products, the daughter substance can easily be obtained from the mother substance, instead of from a mixture of many fission products. Important yttrium and lanthanum isotopes can be obtained in this manner from strontium and barium isotopes. The case is similar for the separation of niobium from zirconium, praseodymium from cerium, iodine from tellurium, and for certain platinum metals. If the half-life of the mother substance is much greater than that of the daughter substance, the latter can be separated from the former again and again, almost like milking a cow. The case of the physical removal of the noble gases also falls under the heading of the easy separation of the mother substances while the separation of the decay products would be difficult.

Measuring the Precipitates

The separation and purification of many precipitates, which constituted the investigation of irradiated uranium, involved a great many filtrations, many of which had to be done very rapidly. The usual glass funnels with folded filter paper were not used at all, but simple two-part porcelain funnels have been very valuable for radioactive research. On the left-hand side of the above illustration, such a porcelain funnel with collar is shown both assembled and taken apart. The filters we used were either hardened filters from Schleicher & Schüll, or, more frequently, filter membranes from the Membranfiltergesellschaft in Göttingen. In most cases porcelain funnels with a diameter of 4 centimeters were used; if the amounts of precipitates were larger, funnels with a diameter of 7 centimeters were used. They can be bought from the Staatliche Porzellanmanufaktur in Berlin in these two sizes. Similar laboratory ware, but of glass, is manufactured by Schott & Co.

Since all precipitates are siphoned off, one need not worry about the leakage of liquid; the two parts of the porcelain filter

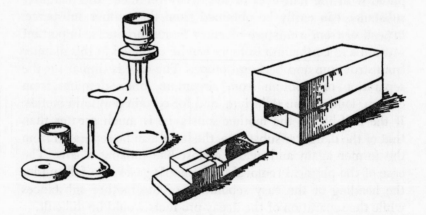

Some of the laboratory equipment used in the chemical separation of the elements and isotopes produced by the fission of uranium

hold tight. The filtration itself is very fast, as is the washing; near the end of the washing the upper part of the funnel is removed and the rim of the filter is washed. After drying (the temperature must be below 150 degrees centigrade in the case of membranes) one then has the smooth filter that can be measured in the counter. Prior to measuring, it is practical to cover the filter with a very thin layer of cellophane, which was furnished by Kalle & Co. in Biebrich am Rhine.

Measuring the activity is done in the customary manner with a Geiger-Müller counter. To protect the counter at least partially against gamma rays and cosmic rays it is put into a heavy lead box (on the right side of the illustration). If intensity of activities is to be compared or if readings have to be taken over a protracted period, every measurement should be preceded by a reading of a thin layer of uranium oxide or a piece of uranium glass, so that all measured activities can be calculated in accordance with the same standard.

If enough counters are available, it is advisable to have, in addition to the standard 100-micron counter, a thin-walled (5- or 10-micron) counter for the detection of easily absorbed soft beta rays. The "softness" of such radiation often permits conclusions as to the purity of a given preparation. It is also advisable for readings of a decline that lasts months or years to use counters that are *not* used for measuring the other precipitates. The latter work imposes much use on a counter and counters used for this purpose might not be as precise as those that are used only for quantitative counts from time to time.

As regards the explanation of the measured-activity curves, everything necessary was said in the preceding report (Appendix II), and at this point it is only necessary to make reference to that.

Biographical Notes

Abelson, Philip Hauge (born Tacoma, Washington, April 27, 1913). Studied at Washington State College and at the University of California, receiving his doctorate in 1939. Took part in atomic-energy research; suggested uranium hexafluoride as the uranium compound best suited for the thermal diffusion principle for enriching uranium with its isotope uranium-235. Co-discoverer of element no. 93, neptunium.

Baeyer, [Johann Friedrich Wilhelm] Adolf von (born Berlin, October 31, 1835; died Starnberg, Bavaria, August 20, 1917). The son of a general who was chief of the Geodetic Institute in Berlin, von Baeyer studied chemistry at the University of Heidelberg under Robert W. Bunsen. He discovered the barbiturates and synthesized indigo. In 1875 he was called to the University of Munich to succeed Justus von Liebig. For his work in synthetic organic chemistry he was awarded the 1905 Nobel Prize in chemistry.

Becquerel, Antoine Henri (born Paris, December 15, 1852; died Le Croisic, France, August 25, 1908). Intrigued by the discovery of X rays, Becquerel experimented with fluorescent substances to see if they emitted X rays as well as visible light. Fluorescence was then believed to be caused by sunlight, but Becquerel reasoned that if a compound emitted X rays, they should fog a photographic plate which had been wrapped in black paper capable of keeping out all visible light as well as ultraviolet rays. He exposed the plates to potassium uranyl sulfate and they were fogged even when the sun did not shine.

266

This discovery, made in early March 1896, started research on radioactive substances. Becquerel shared the 1903 Nobel Prize in physics with the Curies (*q.v.*).

Bohr, Niels [Henrik David] (born Copenhagen, October 7, 1885; died Copenhagen, November 18, 1962). Studied at the University of Copenhagen and, after receiving his doctorate in 1911 went to England to work under Rutherford (*q.v.*). In 1916 he became professor of physics at the University of Copenhagen. Bohr improved on Rutherford's concept of atomic structure, making the structure agree with the quantum theory of Planck (*q.v.*); he was awarded the 1922 Nobel Prize in physics. While in the United States in 1939 for a scientific conference, he heard of Lise Meitner's announcement of the true meaning of Hahn's work and soon added the discovery that it was isotope uranium-235 that fissioned. He returned to Denmark, and, after the occupation of that country by the Germans, escaped to England and thence to the United States, where he became part of the atomic-energy research team. In 1955 he organized the first Atoms for Peace Conference in Geneva.

Boltwood, Bertram Borden (born Amherst, Massachusetts, July 27, 1870; died Hancock Point, Maine, August 15, 1927). Studied at Yale University and received his doctorate there in 1897; he spent most of his life at Yale. He became interested in radioactivity and was among the first to suspect that one radioactive element will change into another one. Since stable lead seemed to be the final product, Boltwood was the first to suggest (in 1907) that radioactive decay might be used for dating the age of the earth's crust. Overwork and nervous strain caused him to end his life by suicide.

Bragg, Sir William Henry (born Wigton, England, July 2, 1862; died London, March 12, 1942). Studied at King William's College (Isle of Man) and later at Cambridge University under J. J. Thomson (*q.v*). In 1886 he went to Australia as professor of physics at Adelaide University and remained twenty-two years. Setting out to measure the distance that alpha particles could travel through a substance without being absorbed, he showed that particles from different substances had very definite "ranges." This suggested radioactive breakdown in stages, since the alpha particles from different substances evidently had different energies. After his return to England he and his son (William Lawrence Bragg, born Adelaide, March 31, 1890) became interested in the work with X rays started by Max von Laue (*q.v.*). Father and son shared the 1915 Nobel Prize in physics. In 1935 Bragg, Sr., was elected President of the Royal Society; Bragg, Jr., became a professor of physics at Cambridge in 1938 and was knighted in 1941.

Brooks, Harriet (born Montreal, 1879; died Montreal, April 17, 1933). Miss Brooks attended McGill University in her native city and received a B.A. degree in 1898. She then became an assistant of Ernest Rutherford (*q.v.*) and took part in his early researches on radon and its decomposition products. She may have been the first researcher to have observed the phenomenon of radioactive recoil, though the observation was not followed up. After becoming Mrs. Frank Pitcher, she discontinued active research.

Chadwick, Sir James (born Manchester, England, October 20, 1891). Received the M. Sc. degree from Victoria University in Manchester and worked under Rutherford (*q.v.*), beginning 1911. Went to Germany to work with Geiger (*q.v.*) and was interned for the duration of World War One. Returning to England in 1919, he resumed work with Rutherford at the Cavendish Laboratory at Cambridge University, where he received his Ph.D. in 1921. In 1932, having checked on some work done by the Joliot-Curies (*q.v.*), he discovered the neutron; this discovery was rewarded with the 1935 Nobel Prize in physics. In 1935 he was appointed professor of physics at the University of Liverpool. He spent part of World War Two in the United States as a member of the British contingent of the atomic-energy research team.

Crookes, Sir William (born London, June 17, 1832; died London, April 4, 1919). Became a student at the Royal College of Chemistry in 1848 but soon after graduation turned his attention to physical phenomena. While investigating selenium ores he discovered the element thallium. In 1875 he invented an improved vacuum tube which still bears his name. It was a Crookes tube that enabled Konrad Roentgen to discover the X rays. Because of his experiments in magnetic deflection of "cathode rays," Crookes should be considered the discoverer of the electron, but he did not carry his work far enough and the concept was at least a decade ahead of its time.

Curie, Marie Sklodowska (born Warsaw, November 7, 1867; died Haute Savoie, France, July 4, 1934). Unable because of political conditions to obtain more than a high-school education in her native country, Marie Sklodowska traveled to Paris to go to the Sorbonne. Married **Pierre Curie** (born Paris, May 15, 1859, discoverer of piezoelectricity) in 1895. The discovery of X rays and the discovery by Becquerel (*q.v.*) which followed caused the Curies to study radioactivity (a term coined by Marie Curie), and they discovered the elements polonium and radium. The Curies and Becquerel shared the 1903 Nobel Prize in physics. Pierre Curie was killed in a traffic accident in Paris on April 19, 1906; therefore the 1911 Nobel Prize (for the discovery of two elements) went to Marie alone. She died of leukemia, possibly the result of long-time exposure to radioactivity.

Debierne, André Louis (born Paris, 1874; died Paris, 1949). Studied at the École de Physique et de Chemie, where he later became its first professor of organic chemistry. He was a close friend of the Curie family and helped Mme. Curie to produce the first samples of pure metallic radium. In 1899 he discovered actinium in pitchblende. After World War One he received many official and academic honors (the Legion of Honor, *Professeur titulaire à la Faculté des Sciences,* and Officer of Public Instruction) and, after Mme. Curie's death, took over the presidency of the Laboratoire Curie. In 1946 he retired from this and all other public positions.

Fajans, Kasimir (born Warsaw, May 27, 1887). Studied in Leipzig, Heidelberg, Zurich, and Manchester. Discovered (with O. H. Göhring) the short-lived uranium-X_2 in 1913, naming it brevium. From 1917–1935 Fajans taught physical chemistry at the University of Munich; then, because of Hitler, he left for the University of Michigan. He is the author of several books on nuclear research. He discovered, simultaneously with Soddy (*q.v.*), the law of radioactive displacement by alpha- and beta-ray emissions.

Fermi, Enrico (born Rome, September 29, 1901; died Chicago, November 28, 1954). Studied at the University of Pisa and received his doctorate in 1922, went to Germany for a year, and became professor of physics at the University of Rome. Especially interested in neutrons, which had been discovered by Chadwick (*q.v.*), Fermi found that neutrons slowed down by passing through water or paraffin were more effective. He fissioned uranium but believed that he had created elements beyond uranium. He received the 1938 Nobel Prize in physics. Instead of returning to Italy, the anti-Fascist Fermi sailed from Stockholm for the United States, where he played a leading role in the building of the first atomic pile and the design of the first fission bomb.

Fischer, Emil Hermann (born Euskirchen, Rhineland, October 9, 1852; died Wannsee, near Berlin, July 15, 1919). Attended high school at Bonn and then the universities of Bonn and of Strassbourg, receiving his doctorate in chemistry in 1874. In 1892 he became a professor at the University of Berlin; his research work was almost exclusively devoted to organic chemistry. He received the 1902 Nobel Prize in chemistry. During World War One, he was engaged in organizing the German chemical industry for war production.

Geiger, Hans (born Neustadt an de Haardt, Palatinate, September 30, 1882; died Berlin, September 24, 1945). Geiger is most famous for his invention of the "Geiger counter" in 1913. After receiving his doctorate, he joined Rutherford (*q.v.*) as assistant in the early 1900s and worked with him until the outbreak of World War One. He then returned to Germany, where he served in the heavy artillery. In 1929 he became professor of physics at the University of Tübingen and did not leave Germany again.

Giesel, Friedrich (born Winzig, Silesia, 1852; died Braunschweig, 1927). Giesel was the son of a physician, and though Otto Hahn once called him the Father of German Radium Research, Giesel was mainly a "practical" chemist. He studied at the Royal Gewerbeakademie in Berlin, where the industrial utilization of discoveries was stressed. In 1875 he became a researcher at the Experiment Station of German Alcohol Producers and then had an industrial job with a chemical factory. In 1874 he obtained his doctorate from the University of Göttingen and then became assistant to Professor Liebermann at the Gewerbeakademie. Four years later he became chief chemist of the Quinine Factory in Braunschweig. After hearing of the discovery of radium, he began to produce radium and radium preparations as a side line; his success in this "side line" was such that he was given the rank of titular professor and of Honorary Doctor of Engineering. A radiation carcinoma on his left index finger is blamed for his death in 1927.

Goldschmidt, Victor Moritz (born Zürich, January 27, 1888; died Oslo, March 20, 1947). Studied at the University of Oslo (where his father was professor of chemistry) and took his Ph.D. in 1911. Specializing in the minerals of the earth's crust, he joined the faculty of the University of Göttingen in 1929. He used the new information on atoms to work out a system of predicting what elements must be present in what minerals, thus pioneering the science of geochemistry. Because of Hitler, Goldschmidt returned to Oslo in 1935, then had to flee to England. He finally returned to Oslo, but cancer terminated his life not long afterward.

Haber, Fritz (born Breslau, Silesia, December 9, 1868; died Basel, Switzerland, January 29, 1934). Studied at the University of Berlin under Robert W. Bunsen and received his doctorate in chemistry. His studies of the chemical processes in the flame of a Bunsen burner led him to invent a method of utilizing the nitrogen of the atmosphere for fertilizers and explosives. In 1911 he was made director of the Kaiser Wilhelm Institute for Physical Chemistry. For his successful synthesis of ammonia, he was awarded the Nobel Prize in chemistry in 1918. During World War One he designed the principle used in the chlorine gas attacks along the western front. In spite of his wartime services, he was exiled by Hitler, and after a short stay in England he went to Switzerland where he died.

Heisenberg, Werner Karl (born Duisburg, Prussia, December 5, 1901). Studied at the University of Munich, where he took his doctorate in 1923. Somewhat later, he joined Niels Bohr (*q.v.*), giving special study to the structure of the atom. He is best known for his "uncertainty principle," announced in 1927. After Chadwick (*q.v.*) had discovered the neutron, Heisenberg was the first to state that this discovery eliminated the need for assuming the presence of electrons in the nucleus of an atom. In charge of atomic research in Germany during World War Two, Heisenberg (deliberately?) undermined his own position by stating that an atomic power reactor (in modern terminology) was more probable than an atomic explosion; naturally this eliminated such priorities as he might have received. He is now director of the Max Planck Institute for Physics at Göttingen.

Hévésy, Georg von (born Budapest, August 1, 1885; died Freiburg, Germany, July 5, 1966). Studied at the University of Freiburg, receiving his doctorate in 1908. He then worked successively with Fritz Haber, Ernest Rutherford, and Niels Bohr. While working under Bohr, he discovered element no. 72, which was named hafnium from the Latin name of Copenhagen. Von Hévésy originated the "tracer method" in biology, by which radioactive atoms are introduced into living organisms and their progress observed. However, the method became useful only after the discovery of artificial radioactive isotopes. In 1943 von Hévésy fled to Sweden, where he taught at the University of Stockholm. He received the 1943 Nobel Prize in chemistry.

Joliot-Curie, [Jean] Frédéric (born Paris, March 19, 1900; died Paris, August 14, 1958) and **Irène** (née Curie, born Paris, September 12, 1897; died Paris, March 17, 1956). Irène Curie, the elder daughter of Pierre and Marie Curie, worked as assistant to her mother and thus met Jean Frédéric Joliot, another assistant. They were married in 1926 and worked as a scientific team, adopting the name Joliot-Curie. They almost discovered the neutron and succeeded (1934) in discovering artificial radioactivity, receiving the 1935 Nobel Prize in chemistry. During World War Two the Joliot-Curies remained in France in the resistance movement; after the war they built the first French nuclear reactor. Irène, like her mother, died of leukemia.

Laue, Max von (born near Coblenz, October 9, 1879; died Berlin, April 23, 1960). Studied at the University of Strassbourg, obtained his doctorate in 1903 and became assistant to Max Planck (*q.v.*). In 1909 he became a professor at the University of Munich. He was interested in X rays, the true nature of which was then still in doubt, especially because their wavelength could not be measured. In 1912, by sending X rays through a crystal of zinc sulfide, von Laue established both the nature and the wavelength of X rays and received the 1912 Nobel Prize in physics for his work. He was professor of theoretical physics at the University of Berlin from 1919 until 1943, when he resigned as a political protest. After World War Two he became director of the Max Planck Institute for Physical Chemistry at Göttingen.

Lawrence, Ernest Orlando (born Canton, South Dakota, August 8, 1901; died Palo Alto, California, August 27, 1958). Studied at the University of South Dakota and obtained his doctorate from Yale in 1925. Joined the faculty of the University of California in 1927 and stayed there until his death. He received the Nobel Prize in physics in 1939 for having invented the cyclotron for accelerating protons. During World War Two Lawrence was busy with one of the several possible methods for producing uranium-235; after the war he returned to nuclear research.

McMillan, Edwin Mattison (born Redondo Beach, California, September 18, 1907). Studied at the California Institute of Technology, obtained his doctorate from Princeton University in 1932, and immediately joined the faculty of the University of California. In 1940, in collaboration with Abelson (*q.v.*), he discovered the element neptunium. During World War Two he was engaged in atomic-bomb research, mainly on research devices; he invented the synchrocyclotron. Shared the 1951 Nobel

Prize in chemistry with Glenn T. Seaborg (*q.v.*) for their work on elements beyond uranium.

Meitner, Lise (born Vienna, November 7, 1878). After obtaining her doctorate in Vienna, Lise Meitner went to Berlin in 1907 to attend Max Planck's (*q.v.*) lectures and remained to work with Otto Hahn until 1938. She was co-discoverer (with Hahn) of protactinium. Uranium fission had just been accomplished when Lise Meitner was forced to leave Germany in 1938, and she announced it in January 1939 from Stockholm. She was in the United States for a short time after World War Two, but returned to Stockholm; she has been a citizen of Sweden since 1949.

Moissan, Ferdinand Frédéric Henri (born Paris, September 28, 1852; died Paris, February 20, 1907). Apprenticed to a pharmacist at the age of 18, Moissan became interested in chemistry and studied as a "working student." Because his teacher had tried unsuccessfully to isolate fluorine, Moissan decided to try and in 1886 succeeded. His discovery brought him a professorship at the School of Pharmacy in Paris, then a professorship at the University of Paris, and finally the 1906 Nobel Prize in chemistry. Moissan was the first to succeed in making artificial diamonds; the story that his assistant surreptitiously added a tiny natural diamond to the preparation is no longer credited.

Moseley, Henry Gwyn-Jeffries (born Weymouth, Dorsetshire, November 23, 1887; killed by enemy action during Gallipoli campaign, August 10, 1915). Studied at Eton and Oxford and worked under Rutherford (*q.v.*) for some time. While studying the X-ray spectra of various elements, Moseley conceived the idea that the number of electric charges in the nucleus was more important than the atomic weight of an element. By introducing the "atomic number" (equal to the number of charges in the nucleus) Moseley produced the only major improvement of Mendeleyev's Periodic Table; without this rearrangement of the table, atomic reactions would make no sense.

Nernst, Walter (born Briesen, West Prussia, June 25, 1864; died Berlin, November 18, 1941). Studied at the University of Berlin and received his doctorate in 1887, became professor of physical chemistry at the University of Göttingen in 1891, and assumed the same position at the University of Berlin in 1905. In 1906 he announced the "third law of thermodynamics," which states that entropy approaches zero at the temperature of absolute zero. For this work he received the 1920 Nobel Prize in chemistry. As an inventor he is best known for the "Nernst lamp," which produced strong light from weak currents but could not compete with the later improvements of the ordinary light bulb.

Ostwald, Friedrich Wilhelm (born Riga, Latvia, September 2, 1853; died Leipzig, April 4, 1932). Studied at the University of Dorpat (now Tartu), receiving his doctorate in 1878, and was appointed a professor at the University of Riga in 1881. In 1887 he accepted a professorship at the University of Leipzig, where he remained till his death, except for one year at Harvard as an exchange professor. He received the 1909 Nobel Prize in chemistry for his work on catalysis. The latter part of his life was devoted to the theory of colors and the philosophy of science.

Pauli, Wolfgang (born Vienna, April 25, 1900; died Zurich, December 15, 1958). Studied at the University of Munich, obtaining his doctorate in 1921. After working for some time with Niels Bohr (*q.v.*), he became a professor at the University of Hamburg in 1923. Though famous for postulating the neutrino as an additional subatomic particle (proton, neutron, electron, and positron were accepted), he received the 1945 Nobel Prize in physics for his theoretical work explaining the chemical characteristics of the rare earth metals. Pauli became a citizen of the United States in 1946; he died during a trip to Europe.

Planck, Max [Karl Ernst Ludwig] (born Kiel, April 23, 1858; died Göttingen, October 3, 1947). Studied at the University of Berlin under Hermann von Helmholtz and Gustav R. Kirchhoff. He was successively professor of physics at the universities of Munich and Kiel; in 1889 he succeeded his teacher Kirchhoff at the University of Berlin where he remained until his retirement in 1926. In 1900 Planck conceived the idea that radiation, like matter, should exist in "particles"; he named these particles "quanta." He received the 1918 Nobel Prize in physics for his "quantum theory." He became president of the Kaiser Wilhelm Society in 1930. He survived the Hitler regime as well as World War Two and was taken into protective custody by American forces in 1945. When the Kaiser Wilhelm Society was re-established in West Germany after the war, it was renamed the Max Planck Society at the request of the Allies.

Ramsay, Sir William (born Glasgow, October 2, 1852); died High Wycombe, England, July 23, 1916). Studied chemistry in Germany under Robert W. Bunsen and received his Ph.D. from the University of Tübingen in 1873. Became professor of chemistry at University College in Bristol in 1880; moved to same position at University College in London in 1887. His fame rests mainly on his discovery of the noble gases—helium, neon, argon, krypton, and xenon—during the period from 1892 to 1900; he received the 1904 Nobel Prize in chemistry for these discoveries. He was knighted in 1902. In collaboration with Soddy (q.v.), he established in 1903 that natural radioactive decay produces helium.

Richards, Theodore William (born Germantown, Pennsylvania, January 31, 1868; died Cambridge, Massachusetts, April 2, 1928). Studied at Harvard University and obtained his doctorate in chemistry for a dissertation on the relative atomic weights of hydrogen and oxygen. Worked in Germany for some time but refused a professorship at the University of Göttingen in favor of Harvard, where he became professor of chemistry in 1894. As a researcher he continued what he had begun as a student, devoting his life to the determination of the atomic weight of the chemical elements; he received the 1914 Nobel Prize in chemistry for this work. Among his greatest achievements was the determination of the various isotopes of lead by chemical means.

Rutherford, Ernest (born Nelson, New Zealand, August 30, 1871; died London, October 19, 1937). Studied first at New Zealand University, then, on a scholarship, at Cambridge under J. J. Thomson (q.v.). Becoming interested in the new field of radioactivity, he discovered that radioactive substances emit three kinds of "rays"; he named positively charged rays "alpha," negatively charged rays "beta," and rays that did not show any charge "gamma." Together with Soddy (*q.v.*) Rutherford traced the chains of decay of uranium and thorium and evolved the concept of the half-life. He was awarded the 1908 Nobel Prize in chemistry; at the same time he left McGill University, Montreal, where he had worked for some years, and went to Manchester University. Achieved first nuclear transmutation (nitrogen into hydrogen and oxygen) in 1917. Became professor of physics at Cambridge in 1919 and was president of the Royal Society from 1925 to 1930. In 1931 he was made a baron and took the name Lord Rutherford of Nelson.

Seaborg, Glenn Theodore (born Ishpeming, Michigan, April 19,1912). Studied at the University of California, received his doctorate there in 1937, and then joined the faculty. In 1940 he joined McMillan (*q.v.*) in research on elements beyond uranium and took over when McMillan left in 1941. Seaborg and his co-workers discovered most of the elements beyond no. 93 (neptunium), and Seaborg and McMillan shared the 1951 Nobel Prize in chemistry for this work. (See also the Introduction to this book.)

Segrè, Emilio (born Tivoli, Italy, February 1, 1905). Studied at the University of Rome, obtaining his doctorate in 1928. Co-worker of Fermi (*q.v.*) in the experiments involving neutron bombardment of elements, Segrè was especially interested in the then undiscovered element no. 43, which he found in a sample of irradiated molybdenum, given to him by Lawrence (*q.v.*); the new element was named technetium. He went to the United States in 1938 and became a citizen in 1944. He was among the first to synthesize element no. 85, called astatine. In 1955 Segrè and Owen Chamberlain succeeded in creating the antiproton, for which they received the 1959 Nobel Prize in physics.

Soddy, Frederick (born Eastbourne, Sussex, September 2, 1877; died Brighton, Sussex, September 22, 1956). Studied at Oxford and then joined Rutherford (*q.v.*) at McGill University in Montreal. The two began to suspect that heavy elements undergo a radioactive decay so that different elements are formed in the course of time. After his return to England, Soddy worked with Sir William Ramsay (*q.v.*); they proved that helium was a product of radioactive decay. Disturbed about the large number of radioactive elements that could not be fitted into the Periodic Table, Soddy realized in 1913 that different "elements" might emit different radiation but have the same chemical composition, thus introducing the concept of isotopes. One year later he proved, as Boltwood (*q.v.*) had suggested ten years earlier, that lead is the final link in a decay chain. He shared the 1921 Nobel Prize for his discovery of isotopes. He retired from the University in 1936, devoting his remaining years to political theories.

Strassman, Fritz (born Boppard, Rhineland, February 22, 1902). Studied inorganic chemistry at the Johann Gutenberg University in Mainz from 1920 to 1925. He received his doctorate from the Engineering College of Hanover in 1929. Soon after that he joined Otto Hahn. He is now chairman of the Institute of Inorganic Chemistry and Nuclear Physics at the University of Mainz.

Szilard, Leo (born Budapest, February 11, 1898; died La Jolla, California, May 30, 1964). Obtained his doctorate from the University of Berlin in 1922 and joined the faculty, remaining until Hitler came to power. In 1934 Szilard went to England and began theoretical work in the field of nuclear physics. He conceived the idea of a chain reaction but worked with the wrong elements; Hahn's discovery of uranium fission put him on the right track. He was one of the scientists who made Einstein write to the President of the United States about the possibility of an atomic bomb and the one who personally transmitted the letter to the White House. After World War Two Szilard became professor of biophysics at the University of Chicago. His advocacy of a nuclear test ban was recognized by the Atoms for Peace award in 1959.

Thomson, Sir Joseph John (born Cheetham Hall, near Manchester, England, December 18, 1856; died Cambridge, England, August 30, 1940). Entered Cambridge University in 1876 and stayed there for the rest of his life, becoming professor of physics in 1884. Working with highly evacuated cathode-ray tubes, he was able to show that the "cathode rays" consisted of particles and also to determine their mass as compared to a hydrogen atom; this was the discovery of the electron. Thomson's concept of the atomic nucleus was superseded by that of his pupil Rutherford (*q.v.*). Later he worked with neon gas and found that an electrically deflected stream of neon atoms split into two streams, the first indication that Soddy's (*q.v.*) concept of isotopes also held true for nonradioactive substances.

Urbain, Georges (born Paris, April 12, 1872; died Paris, November 5, 1938). Received his Ph.D. from the University of Paris in 1899. His work was mainly concerned with the rare earth elements and he discovered lutecium, the heaviest of the rare earth metals. In 1914 he traveled to Oxford to see Moseley (*q.v.*) and was enormously impressed with Moseley's X-ray analysis of a mixture of rare earth elements he had brought with him. One might say that he spent the rest of his life expounding Moseley's discoveries.

Willstätter, Richard (born Karlsruhe, August 13, 1872; died Locarno, Switzerland, August 3, 1942). Studied at the University of Munich under von Baeyer (*q.v.*), obtained his doctorate in 1894, and then became von Baeyer's private assistant. In 1905 he became a professor at the University of Zurich. He worked mainly on plant pigments (especially chlorophyll); receiving the 1915 Nobel Prize in chemistry for this work. During World War One he worked with his friend Fritz Haber (*q.v.*), designing gas masks. After the war he worked mainly on enzymes. He resigned from the university in 1925 and in 1939 went to Switzerland.

Synoptic Calendar

Heinrich Hahn, father of Otto, moves to Frankfurt am Main	1866	
	1870– 1871	Franco-Prussian War, Napoleon III abdicates Sept. 4, France becomes republic, Germany becomes empire
	1871	Frankfurt am Main becomes part of the German Empire
	1878	Lise Meitner born November 7 in Vienna
Otto Hahn born March 8 in Frankfurt am Main	1879	
	1885	Georg von Hévésy born August 1 in Budapest. Niels Bohr born October 7 in Copenhagen
	1886	Clemens Winckler discovers germanium, February 6
	1887	Henry Gwynn-Jeffries Moseley born November 23 in Weymouth, England
	1888	Accession of Kaiser Wilhelm II
	1891	James Chadwick born October 20 in Manchester, England
	1894	Discovery of argon announced by Sir William Ramsay and John W. S. Rayleigh
	1895	Discovery of helium announced by Ramsay

Graduates from Klinger Ober-realschule in Frankfurt; enrolls at University of Marburg an der Lahn	1897	Irène Curie born September 12 in Paris
Transfers to University of Munich	1898	Discoveries of krypton, neon, and xenon announced (May to July) by Ramsay and Travers. Polonium discovered by Marie Curie (July). Radium discovered by Pierre and Marie Curie (December); thorium (known since 1829) announced to be radioactive by Mme. Curie and (independently) by G. C. Schmidt
	1899	Actinium discovered by André Debierne
	1900	Frédéric Joliot born March 19 in Paris. "Radon" (radium emanation) discovered by Friedrich Ernst Uranium-X discovered by Sir William Crookes
Receives his Ph.D. *magna cum laude* from University of Marburg for a dissertation in organic chemistry. Joins 81st Infantry Regiment (stationed in Frankfurt) October 1 for one-year term of military service	1901	Enrico Fermi born September 29 in Rome
Becomes assistant to Professor Theodor Zincke October 1 for a two-year period	1902	
Goes to London to work in Sir William Ramsay's Institute	1904	
Discovers radiothorium in London. Goes to Montreal in fall to work with Ernest Rutherford	1905	
Discovers radioactinium (Montreal, spring). Leaves Canada to join Emil Fischer's Institute in Berlin	1906	Pierre Curie killed April 19 in traffic accident in Paris
Discovers mesothorium. Becomes Privatdozent for Chemistry at University of Berlin. On	1907	

September 28 meets Lise Meitner; beginning of a 30-year collaboration

Development of the method of radioactive recoil and other research methods in "radiochemistry"	1907–1909	
With H. Geitel, represents Germany at first official meeting of International Radium Standard Commission in Paris (March)	1912	Lise Meitner becomes assistant to Max Planck (fall). Opening (October 23) of Kaiser Wilhelm Institute for Chemistry in Dahlem
Marries Edith Junghans March 22	1913	Existence of isotopes recognized by Frederick Soddy
Drafted as vice-sergeant	1914	August 1: beginning of World War One
Promoted to lieutenant	1915	Henry G.-J. Moseley dies in combat; Dardanelles August 10
	1916	Sir William Ramsay dies at High Wycombe, Buckinghamshire, England, July 23
Assigned to special group at headquarters	1917	United States enters war April 6
With Lise Meitner, announces discovery of proto-actinium (protactinium)	1918	Armistice ending World War One signed November 11, Germany becomes a republic
	1919	First nuclear transformation (nitrogen into oxygen and hydrogen) achieved by Rutherford (spring). Sir William Crookes dies April 4 in London. Lord Rayleigh dies June 30 in Witham, Essex, England. Emil Fischer dies July 15 in Berlin
Only son, Hanno, born April 9. Announces discovery of uranium-Z, first nuclear isomer. Receives Emil Fischer Medal from Society of German Chemists	1922	
	1927	Bertram B. Boltwood dies August 15 at Hancock Point, Maine

	1932	Discoveries of positron (Carl David Anderson), neutron (Sir James Chadwick), and "heavy hydrogen" of mass number 2 (H. C. Urey, F. G. Brickwedde, and G. M. Murphy)
"Visiting professor" at Cornell University, Ithaca, New York, February to June. Becomes temporary director of Haber's Institute	1933	Hitler comes to power Fritz Haber leaves Germany
	1934	Fritz Haber dies January 29 in Switzerland Marie Curie dies July 4 in Paris Frédéric and Irène Joliot-Curie announce discovery of artificial radioactivity Enrico Fermi and co-workers irradiate most elements with neutrons and announce the discovery of "elements beyond uranium"
Hahn, Strassmann, and Meitner repeat Fermi's experiments; at first confirm the transuranian elements and believe they have discovered several isotopes of radium	1935– 1938	
	1937	Ernest Rutherford (Lord Rutherford of Nelson) dies October 19 in London
Hahn awarded Canizzaro Prize by Royal Academy of Science in Rome	1938	Anschluss, bringing Austria under Hitler (March 11). Lise Meitner leaves Germany (summer) and goes to Sweden via The Netherlands
Hahn and Strassmann announce fission of uranium	1939	September 1: Hitler orders invasion of Poland; beginning of World War Two
	1940	Neptunium, first true element beyond uranium, discovered by Philip H. Abelson and Edwin

M. McMillan; plutonium (the element beyond neptunium), by Glenn T. Seaborg and associates. Manhattan project under way

Hahn awarded Copernicus Prize by University of Königsberg — 1941 — Pearl Harbor bombed December 7; United States enters war

Awarded Cothenius Medal by German Academy of Naturalists at Halle — 1943

Arrested, along with colleagues, April 25 by United States and British forces; interned near Cambridge, England. Awarded 1944 Nobel Prize in Chemistry during internment — 1945 — War in Europe ends May 8 First test explosion of a fission bomb July 16 near Alamogordo, New Mexico. Operational use of fission bombs over Hiroshima (August 6) and Nagasaki (August 9). End of World War Two, August 15

Returns to West Germany; becomes president of Kaiser Wilhelm Society in British Zone of Occupation. Receives Nobel Prize in Stockholm (December) — 1946

1947 — Max Planck dies October 3 in Göttingen

Becomes president of Max Planck Society — 1948 — Max Planck Society founded in April, succeeding Kaiser Wilhelm Society

Receives Max Planck Medal, Goethe Medal of the city of Frankfurt from Senckenberg Institute, and honorary degrees from University of Frankfurt, University of Göttingen, and Engineering University of Darmstadt — 1949

1950 — Development of hydrogen bomb ordered by President Truman January 31

1952 — (November 1) First test explosion of a hydrogen bomb at Eniwetok atoll

Receives Golden Paracelsus Medal from Swiss Chemical Society	1953	
	1954	*Nautilus,* first atomically propelled submarine, launched January 21 Enrico Fermi dies November 28 in Chicago
Tours American scientific establishments at invitation of Ford Foundation	1955	
Receives Faraday Medal from British Chemical Society and Grotius Medal from Hugo Grotius Foundation	1956	Irène Joliot-Curie dies March 16 in Paris Frederick Soddy dies September 22 in Brighton, England
	1958	Frédéric Joliot-Curie dies August 14 in Paris
Turns presidency of Max Planck Society over to Professor Adolf Butenandt in May Son Hanno killed in automobile accident August 29	1960	
Becomes Honorary President of Max Planck Society	1962	Niels Bohr dies November 18 in Copenhagen
Living in retirement in Göttingen Shares the Enrico Fermi Award with Meitner and Strassmann	1966	Georg von Hévésy dies July 5 in Freiburg

BIBLIOGRAPHY

Publications by Otto Hahn

Publications in German

SCIENTIFIC PAPERS IN PROFESSIONAL JOURNALS

Angewandte Chemie
Künstliche radioaktive Atomarten aus Uran und Thor (with Hans Götte), XLIX (1936), 127 f.

Annalen der Physik
Einige Besonderheiten der bei der Kernspaltung des Urans und Thors entstehenden künstlichen Atomarten, XXXVI (1939), 368–72.

Berichte der Deutschen Chemischen Gesellschaft
Chemische Elemente und Atomarten nach dem Stande der Isotopenforschung, LXV (1932), 1–11; LXVI (1933), 1–12; LXVIII (1935), 1–15; LXIX (1936), 5–20; LXX (1937), 1–16; LXXI (1938), 1–14; LXXII (1939), 1; LXXIV (1941), 24 (with Siegfried Flügge and Josef Mattauch); LXXV (1942), 14–16.

Die Anwendung radioaktiver Methoden in der Chemie, LXVII (1934), 150–63.

Künstliche Radio-Elemente durch Neutronen-Bestrahlung, LXIX (1936), 217–27.

Neue Umwandlungsprozesse bei Neutronen-Bestrahlung des Urans (with Lise Meitner and Fritz Strassmann), same vol. 905–19.

Trans-Urane und ihr chemisches Verhalten (with Lise Meitner and Fritz Strassmann), LXVII (1934), 1374–92.

Chemische Elemente und natürliche Atomarten nach dem Stande der Isotopen- und Kernforschung, LXXIV (1941), 27.

Chemiker Zeitung

Die Auffindung des Radiothors und des Mesothors, LXI (1937), 22.

Geologische Altersbestimmung nach der Strontiummethode, LXVII (1943), 55 f.

Experientia

Auffindung der Uranspaltung, IV (1948), 369–73.

Forschungen und Fortschritte:

Deutung des Heliumvorkommens in nicht α-strahlenden Mineralien, XI (1935), 424 f.

Transurane als künstliche radioaktive Umwandlungsprodukte des Urans (with Lise Meitner), XIII (1937), 298 f.

Die durch Neutronen erfolgte Spaltung des Urans in leichtere Atome (with Fritz Strassmann), XVI (1940), 31.

Einiges über die experimentelle Entwirrung der bei der Spaltung des Urans auftretenden Elemente und Atomarten, XVIII (1942), 115 f.

Geologische Altersbestimmung nach der Strontium-Methode (with Heinz Ewald, Josef Mattauch, and Fritz Strassmann), same vol., 353–55.

Von den natürlichen Umwandlungen des Urans zu seiner künstlichen Zerspaltung, XXI (1945), 19 f.

Helvetica chimica Acta

Moderne Alchemie: Weg über das Unwägbare zum Wägbaren, XXVI (1953), 608–19.

Die Naturwissenschaften

Blei und Helium in ozeanischen Alkalihalogeniden, XX (1935), 86 f.

Entdeckung und Isolierung der Elemente (with Lise Meitner), same vol., 91 and 363.

Halbwertszeit des Protaktiniums, same vol. 505 f.

Entstehungsgeschichte der Bleiarten (with Lise Meitner), XXI (1933), 237 f.

Einfluss des Bleigehalts auf die Verfärbungsvorgänge in Chlornatrium und Chlorkalium bei Radiumbestrahlung (with Hans Joachim Born), XXII (1934), 137 f.

Ursprung des Heliums in Sylvin (KCl) (with Hans Joachim Born), same vol. 138.

Ursprung des Heliums in Beryllmineralien, same vol., 744.

Künstliche Umwandlung des Urans durch Neutronen (with Lise Meitner), XXIII (1935), 37 f., and 230 f.

Künstliche Umwandlung des Thoriums durch Neutronen (with Lise Meitner), same vol., 320.

Künstliche Umwandlungsprodukte beim Uran (with Lise Meitner and Fritz Strassmann), same vol. 544 f.

Vorkommen von Radium in nord- und mittel-deutschen Tiefenwässern (with Hans Joachim Born), same vol., 739 f.

Neue Umwandlungsprozesse bei Bestrahlung des Urans mit Neutronen (with Lise Meitner), XXIV (1936), 158 f.

Herstellung wägbarer Mengen des Strontiumisotops 87 als Umwandlungsprodukt des Rubidiums aus einem kanadischen Glimmer (with Fritz Strassmann and Ernst Walling), XXVI (1938), 475 f.

Lord Rutherford of Nelson, same vol., 737 f.

Neues langlebiges Umwandlungsprodukt in den Trans-Uranreihen (with Lise Meitner and Fritz Strassmann), XXVI (1938), 475 f.

Entstehung von Radiumisotopen aus Uran durch Bestrahlen mit schnellen und verlangsamten Neutronen (with Fritz Strassmann), same vol., 755 f.

Nachweis und Verhalten der bei der Bestrahlung des Urans mittels Neutronen entstehenden Erdalkalimetalle (with Fritz Strassmann), XXVII (1939), 11–15.

Nachweis der Entstehung aktiver Bariumisotope aus Uran und Thorium durch Neutronenbestrahlung [1] (with Fritz Strassmann), same vol., 89–95.

Bruchstücke beim Zerplatzen des Urans (with Fritz Strassmann), same vol., 163 f.

Existenz des Trans-Urans (with Fritz Strassmann), same vol., 451–53.

Spaltprodukte aus der Bestrahlung des Urans mit Neutronen (with Fritz Strassmann), same vol., 529–31.

Einige Bruchstücke beim Zerplatzen des Thoriums (with Siegfried Flügge and Fritz Strassmann), same vol., 544–47.

---

[1] For translation of this paper, see Appendix I.

Verwendung der "Emanierfähigkeit" von Uranverbindungen zur Gewinnung von Spaltprodukten des Urans (with Fritz Strassmann), XXVIII (1940), 54–61.

Verwendung der "Emanierfähigkeit" von Thoriumhydroxyd zur Gewinnung von Spaltprodukten des Thoriums (with Fritz Strassmann), same vol., 61.

Getrennte Abscheidung der bei der Uranspaltung entstehenden Krypton- und Xenon-Isotope (with Fritz Strassmann), same vol., 455–58.

Einige weitere Produkte der Uranspaltung (with Fritz Strassmann), same vol., 543–50.

Kurzlebige Brom- und Jod-Isotope bei der Uranspaltung (with Fritz Strassmann), same vol., 817–20.

Bildung von Zirkon und Protaktinium bei der Bestrahlung des Thoriums mit Neutronen (with Fritz Strassmann), XXIX (1941), 285 f.

Die bei der Uranspaltung auftretenden Molybdän-Isotope (with Fritz Strassmann), same vol., 369 f.

Transmutation der chemischen Elemente, XXX (1942), 245–50.

Isolierung und einige Eigenschaften des Elementes 93 (with Fritz Strassmann), same vol., 256–60.

Die bei der Uranspaltung auftretenden kurzlebigen Barium- und Lanthan-Isotope (with Fritz Strassmann), same vol., 324–28.

Hat in früheren Erdperioden ein radioaktives Cäsium existiert? Barium und Strontium aus Pollucit (with Heinz Ewald, Josef Mattauch, and Fritz Strassmann), same vol., 541 f.

Zum 65. Geburtstag von Otto Hönigschmidt (with Josef Mattauch), XXXI (1943), 121 f.

Einige weitere Spaltprodukte des Urans (with Fritz Strassmann), same vol., 499.

50 Jahre Radium, XXXV (1948), 65–67.

Persönliche Erinnerungen aus der Geschichte der natürlichen Radioaktivität, same vol., 67–74.

Physikalische Zeitschrift

Zerplatzen des Uran- und des Thorkerns in leichtere Atome (with Fritz Strassmann), XL (1939), 673–80.

Chemische Elemente und natürliche Atomarten nach dem Stande der Isotopen- und Kernforschung (with Siegfried Flügge and Josef Mattauch), XLI (1940), 1–14.

Sitzungsberichte der Preussischen Akademie der Wissenschaften
> Radioaktivität und ihre Bedeutung für Fragen der Geochemie, 1932, 2–14.

Abhandlungen der Preussischen Akademie der Wissenschaften
> Zerplatzen des Urankerns durch langsame Neutronen (with Fritz Strassmann), 1939, Heft 12.

> Einiges über die experimentelle Entwirrung der bei der Spaltung des Urans auftretenden Element- und Atomarten [2] (with Hans Götte and Fritz Strassmann), 1942, Heft 3.

> Chemische Abscheidung der bei der Spaltung des Urans entstehenden Elemente und Atomarten [3] (with Fritz Strassmann), 1944, Heft 12.

Scientia (Milan).
> Atomkernprozesse und die Zerspaltung des Urans, LXVIII (1940), 8–13.

Technische Mitteilungen
> Künstliche Radioelemente die bei der Einwirkung von Neutronen auf Uran entstehen, 1939, 554–56.

Zeitschrift für anorganische und allgemeine Chemie
> Die Möglichkeit geologischer Altersbestimmung rubidiumhaltiger Mineralien und Gesteine (with Ernst Walling), 1938, 78–82.

Zeitschrift für Elektrochemie
> Radioaktive und chemische Elementarprozesse, XXXVIII, (1932), 511–18.

> Untersuchungen von Grenzflächenvorgängen nach radioaktiven Methoden, XLIV (1938), 497 f.

Zeitschrift für Kristallographie
> Verschiedene Arten der Abscheidung kleiner Substanzmengen in kristallisierten Salzen und ihre photographische Sichtbarmachung, LXXXVII (1934), 387–416.

Zeitschrift für Naturforschung
> Chemische Abscheidung der bei der Spaltung des Urans entstehenden Elemente und Atomarten (with Walter Seelmann-Eggebert and Fritz Strassmann), I (1946), 545–56.

> 75 Geburtstag von Stefan Mayer, II A (1947), 364.

Zeitschrift für Physik.
> Umwandlungsreihen des Urans die durch Neutronenbestrahlung

[2] For translation of this paper see Appendix II.
[3] For translation of this paper see Appendix III.

erzeugt werden (with Lise Meitner and Fritz Strassmann), CVI (1937), 249–70.

Künstliche Umwandlungsprozesse bei Bestrahlung des Thoriums mit Neutronen (with Lise Meitner and Fritz Strassmann), CIX (1938), 538–52.

Die bei der Uranspaltung auftretenden Molybdän-Isotope (with Fritz Strassmann), CXVII (1941), 789–800.

Hat ein Caesium-Isotop langer Halbwertszeit existiert? (with Heinz Ewald, Josef Mattauch, and Fritz Strassmann), CXX (1943), 598–617.

Die bei der Uranspaltung auftretenden Strontium- und Yttrium-Isotope (with Fritz Strassmann), CXXI (1943), 729–45.

Zeitschrift für Physikalische Chemie

Oberflächenstudien an Eisenoxyden nach der Emaniermethode (with Vera Senftner), CLXX (1903), 191–211.

Zeitschrift des Vereins Deutscher Ingenieure (VDI)

Kettenreaktion des Urans, XC (1948), 9–17.

MISCELLANEOUS PUBLICATIONS, BOOKS, AND PAMPHLETS

Bromderivate des Isoeugenols (doctoral dissertation, 1901).

Was lehrt uns die Radioaktivität über die Geschichte der Erde? Vienna and Berlin: Springer Verlag, 1926.

Natürliche und künstliche Umwandlungen der Atomkerne. Rome: Publications of the Kulturwissenschaftliches Institut at the Palazzo Zuccari, 1941.

Umwandlungen der chemischen Elemente und die Zerspaltung des Urans. Göteborg, Sweden: Chalmers tekniska Högskola Handlingar, No. 28, 1944.

Künstliche Atomumwandlungen und die Spaltung schwerer Kerne. Uppsala: Publications of the German Scientific Institute in Stockholm, 1944.

Nutzbarmachung der Energie der Atomkerne. Munich: Publications of the Deutsches Museum, 1950.

Cobalt 60. Gefahr oder Segen für die Menschheit. Göttingen: Musterschmidt Wissenschaftlicher Verlag, 1955. (Pamphlet.)

Vom Radiothor zur Uranspaltung.[4] Braunschweig: Friedr. Vieweg & Sohn, 1962.

[4] The German edition of *Otto Hahn: A Scientific Autobiography.*

Publications in English

"The Mass of the Particles from Thorium" (with Ernest Rutherford). *Philosophical Magazine,* Vol. XII (1906), 371–78; also in *The Collected Papers of Lord Rutherford of Nelson,* London: George Allen and Unwin, Ltd., 1962, Vol. I, p. 901.

"From the Ponderable to the Imponderable." *Science,* Vol. LXXVII (1933), 397–403.

Applied Radiochemistry. Lectures delivered at Cornell University from March to June 1933. Ithaca, N.Y.: Cornell University Press, 1936.

New Atoms: Progress and Some Memories. A collection of papers edited by W. Gade. New York and Amsterdam: Elsevier Publishing Co., 1950. (Dutch title *Nieuwe Atomen.*)

INDEX

(Page numbers followed by *n* refer to footnotes; those followed by *d* to diagrams.)

293